Elaine Forrestal has a deep appreciation for nature, music – and pirates. She is the author of many highly acclaimed and popular novels for children, and has also written for television. Her novel *Someone Like Me* won the 1998 Children's Book Council Book of the Year Award for Younger Readers. *Graffiti on the Fence* was shortlisted in 2000 for the same award.

Although Elaine lives in Perth, she wrote a large portion of this story while on a barge in France, which she and her husband shared with a number of diverse characters. The particularly vivid flavour of sea-going claustrophobia and tension in parts of the story may be due to this time. Elaine lives just a few paces from the untamed beauty of Scarborough Beach, and this also shows in the rhythms and textures of her prose. But above all, this is an extraordinary, little-known story of a real, larger-than-life figure from Australia's past.

SENIOR HIGH SCHOOL

PENGUIN BOOKS

Also by Elaine Forrestal

The Watching Lake
Straggler's Reef
Someone Like Me
Graffiti on the Fence
Leaving No Footprints
Winning
Deep Water
Stone Circle
Black Earth
Wild Wind

Black Jack Anderson

Elaine Forrestal

BRUNTON SENIOR HIGH SCHOOL
38496.01
F FOR
LIBRARY ✗

PENGUIN BOOKS

PENGUIN BOOKS

Published by the Penguin Group
Penguin Group (Australia)
250 Camberwell Road, Camberwell, Victoria 3124, Australia
(a division of Pearson Australia Group Pty Ltd)
Penguin Group (USA) Inc.
375 Hudson Street, New York, New York 10014, USA
Penguin Group (Canada)
90 Eglinton Avenue East, Suite 700, Toronto, Canada ON M4P 2Y3
(a division of Pearson Penguin Canada Inc.)
Penguin Books Ltd
80 Strand, London WC2R 0RL England
Penguin Ireland
25 St Stephen's Green, Dublin 2, Ireland
(a division of Penguin Books Ltd)
Penguin Books India Pvt Ltd
11 Community Centre, Panchsheel Park, New Delhi – 110 017, India
Penguin Group (NZ)
67 Apollo Drive, Rosedale, North Shore 0632, New Zealand
(a division of Pearson New Zealand Ltd)
Penguin Books (South Africa) (Pty) Ltd
24 Sturdee Avenue, Rosebank, Johannesburg 2196, South Africa

Penguin Books Ltd, Registered Offices: 80 Strand, London, WC2R 0RL, England

First published by Penguin Group (Australia), 2008

10 9 8 7 6 5 4 3 2 1

Text copyright © Elaine Forrestal, 2008

The moral right of the author has been asserted.

All rights reserved. Without limiting the rights under copyright reserved above, no part
of this publication may be reproduced, stored in or introduced into a retrieval system, or
transmitted, in any form or by any means (electronic, mechanical, photocopying, recording
or otherwise), without the prior written permission of both the copyright owner and the
above publisher of this book.

Cover and text design by Megan Baker © Penguin Group (Australia)
Cover photographs by George Silk/Getty Images (sailing boat);
Lars Klove/Getty Images (hand with knife)
Typeset in Cochin 11/16pt by Post Pre-Press Group, Brisbane, Queensland
Printed and bound in Australia by McPherson's Printing Group, Maryborough, Victoria

National Library of Australia
Cataloguing-in-Publication data:
Forrestal, Elaine, 1941- .
        Black Jack Anderson.

        ISBN 9780143005940 (pbk.).

        1. Anderson, John William, 1809?-1835. 2. Pirates -
        Western Australia - Biography. 3. Piracy - Western
        Australia - History. 4. Whalers (Persons) - Western
        Australia - Biography. I. Title.

        364.164092

penguin.com.au

Dedicated to the memory of
Russell Alfred Chandler (1913–1999)
who dubbed himself Peg-leg Pete
the Pirate and, at 83 years of age,
learned to walk again

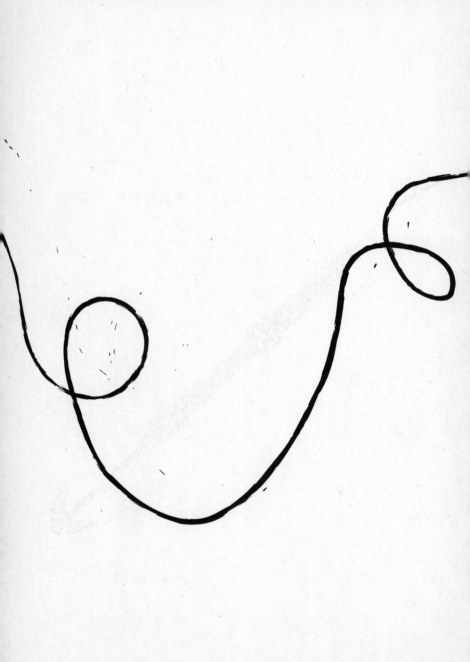

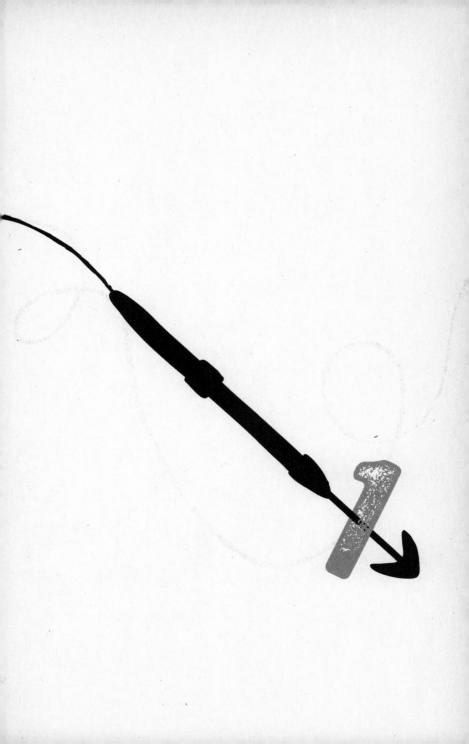

1

ON THE AFTERNOON OF 29 MARCH 1837, PATRICK TAYLOR, JUSTICE of the Peace, was having a rest. The heat had become so oppressive in the roughly hewn cottage overlooking the harbour at King George Sound that he had drawn the curtains in the living room and taken refuge on the couch. But he was not asleep. That would have been too much to hope for.

At first, he ignored the light knocking sounds coming from the vicinity of his front door. Perhaps, if he didn't move, whoever it was would go away and come back later, when the scorching daylight hours had passed. It was not an urgent knock, by any means. Let it wait, he thought. As justice of the peace in the frontier community, he was often called upon to deal with matters that were not really his responsibility.

But the knocking persisted.

Finally, with a disapproving grunt, Patrick got up and opened the door.

Light and heat flooded in. He squinted into the glare, but could see no one. Grumbling to himself, he turned to go back inside. A different sound came from somewhere to his right.

'Huh-hum.' It was a hoarse, strangled sort of cough from vocal cords rarely used.

Patrick Taylor looked again. With eyes now adjusted to the brightness, he saw someone standing on the front porch, a few steps to one side of his door. Wild, unkempt hair framed the man's scarred and weathered face. He wore a faded shirt, open to the waist, and a pair of ragged trousers held together by a grubby sash of cotton cloth. His gnarled and calloused feet were bare.

When the stranger neither moved nor spoke, Patrick felt obliged to ask, 'Were you looking for me?' A runnel of sweat was beginning to slide down Patrick's back. He fervently hoped there was some mistake and that he could quickly get rid of this unsavoury-looking character, but it was not to be.

'I come to report a murder.'

'I beg your pardon?' Patrick Taylor turned his good ear towards the man. In a harbour town like this there would always be violence from time to time, especially if there was a Yankee whaling ship in port. Between the sailors, starved of alcohol and company, and the townsfolk trying to protect their women, tempers often flared and drunken brawls turned nasty. But a quick look out over the harbour confirmed that there were no new arrivals. No swaying masts, creaking ropes or scurrying sailors disturbed the calm of the sleepy port. Patrick was about to redirect him to the barracks, where a dozen soldiers were officially in charge of law and order, when the man spoke again.

'I come to report it,' he insisted. 'The murder of Black Jack Anderson.'

'Black Anderson? But he's been dead these two years past. I heard he leapt into the sea wearing an over-full money belt. Drowned by his own greed for gold, and good riddance to him, and all his kind.' Patrick was relieved that no further action would be needed and he could now go back to his afternoon siesta.

'No, sir, not drowned!' The stranger shook his head with such conviction that his matted hair swept his shoulders like a broom. 'Sure there never was a better swimmer. Nor a man more at home in the sea. This was murder! In cold blood!' The gruff voice rose to a shrill fever-pitch. 'I'm after seein' it with me own eyes, so I am. And not just the one time, neither. Some nights I'm terrified to go to sleep for it all comes back so real! Alive and walkin' around, or lyin' dead – his brains blowed out – I tell ya, he's been givin' me no rest at all.' The man's face was contorted with fear, and with the effort of making such a long speech.

Patrick turned sideways in his open doorway and stretched out his arm. 'You'd better come in,' he said.

2

WITH HIS PEN POISED ABOVE THE POT OF INK, PATRICK TAYLOR looked up at the man who sat ill at ease on the padded chair at the JP's table.

'Name?'

'Gimble – Robert Gimble, me mother named me.' The man turned his head towards the window as if checking for an escape route, but the curtains were still drawn tight against the heat. 'Ah, 'tis a right old time since I heard that name pass anyone's lips,' he muttered to himself.

'G-i-m-b-l-e?' Patrick asked, lifting his pen out of the precious ink that had been carried from England and was irreplaceable before the next shipment arrived – and who could tell when that might be?

Gimble shifted his buttocks on the chair. 'I don't rightly know, sir. I've no book learnin' at all.'

While Patrick wrote *Declaration of Robert Gimble to Patrick Taylor JP in the Town of Albany 29th March 1837*, Gimble thought about his mother, left behind in Ireland so many years before, and wondered if she was still alive.

Was it during his first or second year as a convict in Van

Diemen's Land that the new batch of prisoners had arrived? One day seemed so much like another in the penal colony that it was hard to tell. But one of the new chums came from County Cork. He knew Robert Gimble's mother, and his older brother, Michael. He told stories of Michael, who was still thumbing his nose at the law and living in freedom among their family and friends while Robert languished, in hellish conditions, imprisoned at the bottom of the world.

Michael had needed the help of the smaller, more athletic Robert whenever there were high windows or tight hatches to go through. Quick and agile as a stalking cat, Robert was known as 'Nimble Gimble' for his knack of getting into, and out of, all the grand houses and rich country estates in the south of Ireland. But although Michael could rely on Robert, the reverse was not the case.

During a burglary, the police arrived. Michael scarpered, abandoning the fifteen-year-old Robert to his fate. Captured, found guilty and transported to Van Diemen's Land, the boy grew and toughened in spite of beatings, very little food and a lot of hard labour.

It was all so long ago, but he still missed the noisy company of his eight brothers and sisters and the rough humour that sometimes seemed to be the only thing keeping the family alive. That and the proceeds of Michael's illegal activities.

Homesickness, harsh living conditions and the cruelty of the warders, who wielded their infamous lash for the most petty of misdemeanours, wore Robert down. But he never gave up the idea of escape. He planned it over and over, sometimes with others, sometimes on his own, in his head. Then one day, he saw an opportunity, and seized it.

Life on the run was a constant struggle against the elements, starvation, fatigue and the law. He had looked death squarely in the eye more than once, but this was different. Although he had vowed never to be captured again, the knowledge that was eating away at him had to be imparted. He must take his chances with the justice of the peace.

'Now, about the murder of Black Jack Anderson.' The voice of Patrick Taylor brought him back to the present. 'Two years ago, you say?'

But the story that Nimble Gimble had to tell really began long before that and half a world away from King George Sound.

3

WHILE NIMBLE GIMBLE WAS AVOIDING CAPTURE IN HIGH WINDS AND foaming seas off the coast of Van Diemen's Land, Jack Anderson and his father were enveloped in the thick Atlantic mist that hung like a blanket over the New Bedford docks.

Born John William Anderson in Massachusetts early in the nineteenth century to a mother who died giving birth to him, Jack was raised almost single-handedly by his father, Reuben. Jack went to sea as a cabin boy when he was no more than nine years old, aboard the same ship as Reuben. Now that Jack was seventeen, the ageing Reuben felt that the time had come for him to make his own way in the world.

Christmas 1826 had been particularly bleak along the east coast of North America. Arctic winds had buffeted New Bedford harbour, bringing sheets of rain and sleet that eventually gave way to damp, cloying fog. Whalers preparing their ships for years at sea put aside the sadness of partings from home and family and began to look forward to journeying south into warmer latitudes.

The Andersons were both big men, standing well above

six feet tall and towering over the merchants, delivery boys, messengers and sailors who bustled around the ships in port, like ants around a broken nest. The older man, his shoulders slightly stooped below his tightly curling grey hair, paused beside a three-masted bark and looked up at the name on her bow; *Vigilant*. The bark had recently been converted for whaling. Open troughs for boiling down blubber had been bricked in along the near side of her deck. Sails and rigging were being loaded into pens on the other.

'Yo! Captain Carpo!' Reuben called up to the deck where the captain and another man were obviously engaged in some sort of dispute. The captain stopped mid-sentence and turned towards the dock.

'Yes, yes, all right.' His voice boomed like a foghorn. It was not immediately clear whether he was talking to the man in front of him or the one below, but the old African-American on the dock didn't hesitate. He strode up the gangplank followed by Jack and was on the deck in no time.

'Reuben Anderson! How are you?' The captain clasped his hand and shook it vigorously while Reuben beamed.

'This here's my son Jack,' Reuben said, freeing his hand so that Captain Carpo could accept the one already being offered in greeting by Jack.

'Hmm,' said the captain, running his eyes over the youth. 'A fine strapping lad. Is he as good a seaman as you, Reuben?'

'Surely, Cap'n. Bin sailin' since he be knee-high. I done taught him everythin' I know,' the older Anderson said proudly. 'He can read and write real good, too.'

'I don't think there'll be much call for that where we're

going, Reuben. Still, if he has your wit and but half your courage, he'll likely do all right.'

'You fixna sign him on?'

'I will. And you. It's the least I can do, since I owe you my life,' the captain said.

But Reuben shook his head sadly. 'I can't shimmy up a mast no more, on account o' the rheumatics,' he said.

'Surely not,' the captain replied.

''Fraid so,' Reuben confirmed. 'There be just the boy now.'

The captain turned to Jack. 'Stow your kit and report back to me,' he said, indicating the forecastle and resuming his conversation with Reuben. 'Now, you old sea dog, what do you know?'

The two men compared news and gossip from different ports while Jack made his way to the crew's quarters.

The bark was provided with forward and aft cabins. Two rooms were knocked into one on the starboard side for the use of the captain. The first mate's room was on the port side, opposite, and the second and third mates had their accommodation in the forward cabin where the hammocks of the crew hung in tiered rows. The few possessions that each man carried were stored in drawstring bags hanging from the pegs that held the hammocks.

Some of the men were already playing cards, using the top of a stores-barrel as a table. Others lounged in their hammocks. Jack nodded to those who looked up at him.

Reuben had been a sailor all his life, but after the devastating death of his wife he did not go to sea for seven years. To support himself and his youngest son, he had eked out a living catching and selling fish from the jetties and breakwaters around New Bedford until Jack was old enough to join a ship's crew.

It was a hard, man's world, and the young Jack, always big for his age, learned to fight early in his life. He also learned to swim when a group of idle crewmen threw him off a ship and into the sea. They roared with laughter at the antics the gasping boy employed to stay afloat, before finally throwing him a line and dragging him back on board. Partly to keep him below decks and out of trouble after that, his father taught him to read. Using the Bible in exactly the same way as he himself had been taught by a British sailor of missionary zeal many years before, Reuben tried, at the same time, to instil some moral principles in his wild and often wayward son. But, although he learned quickly enough, in Jack's experience, fists were a much more immediate and less ambiguous form of communication.

4

ONCE THE *VIGILANT* HAD CLEARED THE HARBOUR, HER THREE whaleboats were lowered and the green hands taught their places and how to handle their oars. These open boats, built for speed and buoyancy, were of the Beetle type. Named for the man who originally designed and built them, not for the armoured insect, they were twenty-eight feet in length with four oars and a single sail. A small wooden ramp, fitted inside the hull, allowed the mast that carried this sail to slide in and out of its 'shoe' and be laid horizontally, beside the oarsmen, when not in use.

Jack Anderson was allocated a place in one of these chaser boats in the charge of another African-American. An experienced whaler, John Bathurst was, in many ways, the opposite of Anderson. Small, but wiry, quietly spoken and given to thinking things through, he was, nevertheless, a tough, no-nonsense man.

'I be needin' a volunteer for the harpoon,' he said to his crew of rooky whalers. 'Since the last man's leg got taken off by a rope.' Several men blanched, but Jack Anderson raised his hand. Bathurst nodded. 'Now, you might be thinkin' it ain't possible to miss a critter as big as a whale,' he said. 'But their eye ain't no bigger than a cow's an' they got a great dome of bone for a skull. The man who can land his iron in the exact spot to pierce that skull will be the one who survives – along with the rest of his mates. Look to the dartboard below decks there. Get some practice.'

Already quick and accurate with his fists, Anderson now became skilled at handling a harpoon.

A whale was sighted on the afternoon of 3 March, but it was going quickly to windward and there was no chance to lower the boats. Then a whole school appeared and the bark luffed to the wind, but again the whales were going too fast and there was no chance to lower.

A week went by before another school of whales was sighted on the lee quarter. The ship changed direction to head them off. The weather had turned squally. In driving rain, and under two lower topsails, the bark dashed along at a good pace. But the whales were elusive. All the next day the chase continued, but no whales were taken.

For five weary months, the bark *Vigilant* plied the Atlantic from north to south in search of whales. A small humpback was taken off the coast of California. But after that, none were sighted. They would have to hunt further from home.

South of the equator their stocks of alcohol ran out. Flour and sugar were almost gone and even whalemeat was in short supply.

The ship continued south, following the migration paths of the southern right and humpback whales. During the next month several whales were seen, but none captured. The ship made frequent stops at various ports to replenish supplies. The crew was in poor spirits, when suddenly the cry went up.

'She blows! Look – there!'

The boats were lowered so eagerly that some men were still scrambling to get on board. The oarsmen pulled their hardest and the harpooners stood ready with their long spears. But the whale disappeared before they could get within range. Again and again they were frustratingly close to their prey, only to see it escape into the vast black seas.

Another month went by and the ship went further and further south. They saw icebergs and the bark endured violent storms, sometimes accompanied by squalls of hail. Many of the men came from warmer climates and suffered terribly with the cold. Still there were no whales.

One of the boatsteerers, a tall Kanaka named Thomas, died of exposure up in the rigging. His body thumped to the deck and lay still. Once they had dragged him into the shelter of the forecastle, the men tried in vain to revive him. He was buried at sea and his tasks were divided among the others.

While the bark plunged drearily in heavy seas, under short sail, the men went silently about their work, falling dejectedly into their bunks between times. It seemed that no one had the heart, any longer, for the bawdy songs and time-numbing games that sailors play to stave off boredom.

It was during this period that the captain called for Anderson to come to his cabin. As soon as the young man bent his huge frame to enter, he smelled cooked meat. The remains of the meal that lay on the table made it clear that the captain and his mates had dined well that night. Much better than the foremast hands.

'Come then, Anderson, liven up our evening with a recitation from that Bible of yours.' Anderson stared at the captain. 'Your father says you even have some Chaucer and Shakespeare by heart. I'm sure it would be entertaining to hear them, but perhaps a Bible story tonight? It may even bring us help from on high. Heaven knows we need it.'

It was true that Anderson could read and recite. But only in bars after a good deal of drink had been consumed by everyone present. He had never been asked to plead for help from God. In any case, he had seen so much death, disease and injustice that he had trouble with the notion of a god, loving or otherwise, who intervened in the lives of men. He stood irresolute in the face of the expectant officers.

'All right then,' the captain said finally. 'You shall have a tot of whiskey to lubricate your vocal chords, but mind you don't mention it to the men or we'll have a mutiny on our hands.'

So Anderson began, his deep voice resonating above the sounds of wind and sea as he recited the stories of Jonah and the Whale, Moses at the Red Sea, Peter the Fisherman and Jesus, who calmed and walked upon the water.

It became a nightly ritual. Anderson's watch was changed to make him available for these evening duties. He was given food from the captain's table. Somehow, there was always a decent meal in the captain's cabin, even though the other men were now reduced to eating mouldy biscuits and small portions of leathery salted fish.

Anderson never spoke of the chore he was ordered to perform each evening. But resentment and jealousy spread quickly among the crew, who saw the new chum as unfairly privileged. Old slights, real or imagined, were recalled and quarrels broke out over the most trivial things.

'Sling yo' hook.'

'Eh?'

'Git outta my space, man.' Anderson stood over Mopsy Roso, a whingeing foremast hand.

'Your space, is it?' Sharp intakes of breath were audible in the cramped forecastle.

'You be knowin' damn well . . .' Anderson's voice grew quiet and his heavy eyebrows drew together. It was a danger sign that some had come to recognise, but not Mopsy Roso – or perhaps he decided to ignore it.

'I don't know nuthin',' Roso said defiantly. 'You the boy what knows it all with your readin' and writin' and entertainin' the captain. But I tell ya this, I ain't movin'!'

Anderson regarded Roso with obvious fury. His hands clasped and unclasped at his sides. Then he grabbed Roso, lifted him clear of the floor, swung him around and threw him down like a discarded toy. The outraged Roso leapt to his feet. He came at Anderson with fists flying and thumped rapidly into the tight muscles of the big man's stomach and chest. Anderson stood for a minute, letting the blows rain on him. Then he smashed his massive fist into Roso's face. Blood flowed freely from the sailor's nose.

The sounds of this disturbance brought Captain Carpo to the top of the ladder.

'Anderson!' he commanded. 'I'll see you in my cabin. Roso, get that mess cleaned up.'

A few men grumbled about the injustice, but most just sat there, refusing to move while Mopsy Roso, his face rapidly swelling, lowered a bucket over the side, pulled up the icy sea water and set to work with a cleaning rag.

In the captain's cabin Anderson stood, ill at ease, but refusing to lower his head. His frame took up so much room that Captain Carpo had to squeeze past him to reach his desk.

'Look, Anderson, I warned you about this.'

Anderson shook his head. 'I ain't said nothin'.'

'Then why is it that I suddenly find you at the centre of every argument on board?'

'They mad at me, dinin' in the cabin while they bin fed scraps ain't no dog gonna eat.'

'The devil they are!' Captain Carpo's outrage showed on his face as he studied the young man who stood, legs apart, chin raised defiantly. 'I'll speak to them. And you'll mind your manners.' But all this was immediately forgotten when a call came loud and clear from the crow's nest.

'She blows a-starb'd!'

Without waiting to be dismissed, Anderson ducked out through the doorway. The chaser boats had barely settled in the water before their crews were pulling away.

5

SHOUTS OF 'PULL!' AND 'HEAVE AWAY!' FILLED THE AIR. THE CHASE was on.

The whale was a good size and spouted time after time. With men pulling hard on the oars, the boats closed in. Making the most of every swell to increase their speed, the men brought their craft into a triangle formation with the whale roughly in the middle. Then it sounded.

Silently they waited, rocking on the low swell. In each boat the oars rested in their rowlocks. The boatsteerers stood in the stern, their harpooners crouched at the ready in the bow. Every man scanned the surface of the sea for the first hint of the whale below.

Ten, twenty, thirty minutes passed. The men were getting anxious. Had the slow-moving humpback somehow given them the slip? It didn't seem possible in the clear conditions.

Jack Anderson shifted impatiently. The harpoon rested on his broad shoulder as his black eyes scanned the sea. John Bathurst held the steering oar steady in his hand. His eyes were constantly moving, checking for signs. The whale had been down for forty minutes.

A southerly breeze sprang up. Waves began to mount and it became increasingly difficult to hold the boats in position. By mutual consent they spread out, hoping that at least one would be close to their prey when it did decide to surface.

Then, without warning, the streaming back of the mighty mammal came up directly under Jack Anderson. Half as big again as the boat itself, the moving mountain erupted from the deep. The Beetle was thrown up to almost vertical before sliding off the whale's back, bow first, into the sea. Jack Anderson threw the harpoon with all the force of his huge arm. The shot hit home, but the angle of the boat and his own momentum pitched him into the water. As the whale sank below the surface, Anderson was sucked down. Foaming, blood-red waves closed over his head. With all hands clinging for their lives to the gunwales, there was nothing the others could do to save him.

The harpoon held fast in the whale, but the animal was far from dead. The boat was towed along at terrifying speed through the chop and swell. It took the superhuman efforts of every man on board to prevent it being completely swamped, but no one was prepared to cut the line and lose their catch.

The air was thick with shouts and curses as the other boats closed in on the injured whale. Suddenly Anderson's hand appeared, clutching the harpoon line. Then his head was beside it, his mouth gaping, spitting out blood and water as he hauled himself up along the rope. John Bathurst was closest and helped the wild-eyed Anderson climb back on board. Blood was streaming from cuts to his head and face, and running into his open mouth as he coughed and gasped for air.

'Pull, you lubbers!' Anderson rasped at the stunned crew as he righted himself and grabbed the nearest lance. The crewmen heaved the boat closer to the tiring whale and watched with amazement as Anderson plunged a second shaft in deep. The animal thrashed its mighty tail, causing a wave that almost capsized all three boats and sent clotted blood and spray all over the men. Then it rolled and lay still in the water. 'No man will say Jack Anderson can't finish what he started!' the big man roared. Then he passed out from loss of blood.

Back on the bark, with the whale secured alongside, Captain Carpo ordered Anderson be carried below, where his wounds were dressed and he was told to rest. There was relief and excitement about finally securing a whale, but the jubilant mood on board was somewhat dampened when Anderson's tasks were divided among the others, who were already doing extra work because of the death of Thomas. Even the crew's admiration of Anderson's amazing feat was being tempered, mainly by Roso, with a new suspicion.

'How'd he do that?'

'It ain't possible.' Others muttered or shook their heads.

'I seen it with me own eyes!'

'Aye, you'd never believe it, else.'

'Should'a drowned,' Mopsy Roso complained, as if he had been cheated of the perfect solution to his problems.

'He's a holy man. Bible readin' and that,' one of the men suggested.

'In league with the devil, more like,' the malicious Mopsy declared.

It was unusual, to say the least, for a crewman lost overboard during a chase to survive. But then to turn around and finish off the whale with his own hand! Surely no mere human being could perform such an incredible feat.

There were other rumours. One man had heard that, on a previous voyage, Anderson had been bound and dunked repeatedly into the sea as punishment for stealing, although he protested his innocence.

'Bugger should have drowned that time, too,' the sailor reported. 'But not him. Hauled him up unconscious, cut to ribbons and blue as a mullet around those thick lips o' his. They all thought he was a goner. But minutes later he's coughin', thrashin' his body and spewin' up half the ocean. He was alive all right – and still fightin' like a marlin on a spike.'

The next day, Jack Anderson got up from his sick bed on the *Vigilant* and, although still weak, insisted on doing his share of the work. A deep gash across one cheek bled with any sudden movement and he could barely walk. His speech was thick and slurred. If he hadn't known better, John Bathurst would have said that Anderson was drunk. The other men stayed clear of the big American when they could.

Working beside him, Bathurst was concerned. 'Hey man, you s'posed to take it easy.'

'Easy?' Anderson stared as if he didn't know the meaning of the word.

Bathurst was a skilful seaman. As calm as Anderson was

volatile, as careful as the other man was reckless, he kept his own counsel. While he dismissed as superstitious nonsense the verbal attacks on Anderson, he did not defend him, either. His position as third mate had been hard won, but was now never questioned. It gave him control of one of the Beetles and a seat at the captain's table.

While observing Anderson closely during his recitations in the cabin, Bathurst noticed that, for all his keen intelligence, the young giant lacked the necessary social skills for shipboard life. Anderson was difficult, quick tempered and stubborn. In spite of this, Bathurst felt a grudging sympathy for him.

Not that Anderson needed anyone's sympathy. All whalers were tough men, but Anderson was tougher. He had grown up fighting. Already standing head and shoulders above other children by the age of five, he was teased mercilessly for his clumsy, ungainly body. More used to the company of adults, he was shy and unsure how to behave with anyone his own age – until he learned that a swift punch to the head of his tormentors earned him a certain amount of respect.

By seventeen, hard physical work had honed his muscles, and sojourns in foreign ports had sharpened his instincts. Loud and aggressive, especially when he was drunk, there was, nevertheless, a certain charisma about him. And he was quickly proving to be one of the fastest and most accurate of men with a harpoon.

The sight of Jack Anderson standing, tall as a tree, in the bow of a whaleboat, harpoon poised, roaring his defiance at the elements, was awe inspiring. But the *Vigilant* had so far captured only two whales on this trip. There had been talk of a Jonah☠ on board. Anderson was the obvious suspect. It was not just his book-learning that set him apart. His enormous size, coupled with an unpredictable temper, confused the men. Even when he was quiet there was something of the coiled snake about him, a sense that he was biding his time, but capable of striking with immense ferocity if roused. Most of the crew tried to avoid him, but with the ill-fated ship at the mercy of the weather and needing all hands, there was nowhere to go.

In spite of a howling southerly and choppy seas, the crew of the *Vigilant* set about the task of stripping the blubber from the captured whale. They hacked away with their long, curved blades and threw the slabs into open troughs that lined the port side of the deck. Once the precious oil had been rendered down, it was siphoned into empty stores-barrels, ready to be traded or shipped back to New Bedford if the opportunity arose. With oil in their barrels and meat on their plates once more, the men's spirits lifted. There was talk of America and

---

☠ The biblical prophet, Jonah, disobeyed God's instruction to go to Nineveh and boarded a ship heading in the opposite direction. Before long a mighty tempest sprang up and, when the ship was obviously in danger of sinking, the crew drew lots to find out who was responsible for their dire misfortune. The lot fell upon Jonah, who then suggested that they throw him into the sea. As soon as Jonah was thrown overboard the sea became calm and God sent a great fish which swallowed Jonah whole. After three days and three nights the fish vomited Jonah up, unharmed, onto the beach. Jonah set off immediately for Nineveh.

home. Animosity and suspicion were mostly put aside – for the time being.

The ship was badly in need of repair. On their year-long journey south, storms had shredded her mainsail and spread her timbers. The hull and deck needed resealing.

Captain Carpo plotted a course for the nearest harbour where he could trade oil and whalebone for provisions and make the necessary repairs.

On 28 September 1827 the *Vigilant* sailed into King George Sound where the tiny settlement of Albany was clinging precariously to the south-western edge of Australia.

6

A SCHOONER WAS ALREADY LYING AT ANCHOR IN THE NATURAL harbour at King George Sound. And two other whaleboats, of the same 'Beetle' design as those belonging to the *Vigilant*, were resting, sails furled and masts lying along their gunwales, on the beach above the high-water mark.

Once the *Vigilant*'s anchors were down, her crew wasted no time in breaking out the cargo. They loaded the barrels of oil into their chaser boats and pulled for shore with an enthusiasm that they had not shown in months.

While Captain Carpo sought out the merchant and negotiated the sale of his cargo and the purchase of stores, the men went straight to the pub. The fact that their wages had not yet been paid did not stop them from filling themselves with grog, and, having seen the full barrels and sacks of baleen being landed, the publican was happy to get out his slate for the thirsty whalers.

The brisk south-westerly, blowing across the harbour, ruffling the water and soughing through the rigging of the anchored ships, did not penetrate the crowded room. Inside the pub, smoke from oil lamps, men's pipes and the open fire hung in a cloud below the rafters and swirled about the heads of men from every corner of the known world.

With two ships in the harbour, men of all ages and colours were crammed together, their voices rising to call for more grog or to greet a new arrival. Only the most hardy, and the most desperate, ventured this far south, but they often knew each other. They frequented the same ports, drank in the same pubs and, after a particularly heavy night, had been known to share a cell in the same lock-up.

There was a momentary hush as Black Jack Anderson's giant frame filled up the doorway. Ships were the only available carriers of goods, mail and gossip, but news managed to travel around the world at amazing speed. His height, the intense blackness of his skin and the proud carriage of his head made him an unusual sight. His reputation for violence, but also for skill and daring, was becoming known.

The noise level in the pub quickly rose again as the patrons returned to their drinks and their conversations. It was always the boast of whalers that, by the nature of the work they chose to do, their lives were at risk more often than those of any other occupation. But in this room they were mixing with escaped convicts, shipwrecked sailors who had been marooned on the most distant, desolate shores, and survivors of all sorts of unspeakable horrors.

Bathurst followed Anderson into the pub. The publican, his slate at the ready, asked the two newcomers what they would have.

'Whiskey,' said Anderson, perching his large frame on a square bar-stool, its rough wood smoothed and polished by constant use. 'And none of your watered-down slops.'

The publican nodded. Smiling, he ducked below the counter to bring out the bottle and add the more expensive item to the mounting tally on his slate. Bathurst indicated that he would have the same. There were no more stools available so he stood beside Anderson, whose head was now almost level with his own.

'Off the *Vigilant*, eh?' the man on the next stool addressed the newcomers. His pale blue eyes had the penetrating look that sailors seem to develop after long years of scanning the horizon. Anderson nodded in the man's general direction, and returned to the serious business of getting drunk.

Obviously encouraged, the man said, ''Tis a rum game, whalin',' and smiled at his own play on words. Anderson surveyed his chatty neighbour with impenetrable black eyes. Picking up the heavy glass by its handle he tossed the contents down his throat, then pushed the glass towards the publican who refilled it immediately.

Not satisfied with the response from Anderson, the sailor appealed to a man sitting on the other side of him. 'Ain't it the truth, Gimble?'

'What?' Gimble leaned forward, straining to hear above the din.

'Whalin'. It's a mug's game!' the first man shouted. Since the bar was now about half full of whalers, most of them intent on making up for several very dry months at sea, this remark caused an uproar. Whatever they might feel about their hazardous profession, this sort of talk would never be allowed to go unchallenged.

'Harr! Soft sealers, are ya? Not real men at all!' Jars and tankards were banged down and liquor spilled in the process. Then there were even louder protests over the loss of their precious drinks. It was only a matter of time before the first punch was thrown.

'I warned you not to make trouble!' the publican yelled, reaching across the bar and grabbing the blue-eyed sealer by the front of his shirt.

'I was only sayin'!' The man jerked free, his own newly filled tankard still in his hand. This sudden movement brought him crashing into Anderson. Thick brown liquid flew through the air and caught Black Jack full in the face. In a reflex action, Anderson felled the man.

Knives and pistols were whipped out. Anderson rose slowly from the stool. A space opened up around him as men drew aside. John Bathurst bent over the fallen man who lay still, eyes staring vacantly.

'Dead.'

The word penetrated the smoky air and ricocheted around the room.

Dead? Dead! Dead.

7

ANDERSON LOOKED DOWN. THE EXPRESSION ON HIS FACE PASSED from shock to resignation before he stepped over the man and walked out the door. The crowd, stunned into silence, parted and let him through, then leaned in to stare again at the body on the floor.

'Hey! You! Come back!' From behind the bar, the publican's shout triggered the first reaction.

'Go after him!' Several voices demanded this of no one in particular, but a dead body on the floor of the bar was a more immediate problem. The man striding out into the darkness would not get far. A whole continent, inhabited only by Aborigines, spread out to the north. The 3000 miles of land to the east, between King George Sound and Botany Bay, had never been crossed by Europeans. And the vast Southern Ocean, the full extent of which was known only to the whales, lay to the south. There was no rush to follow the Yankee whaler. Not while there was no law court in the harbour settlement and most of the soldiers, stationed there to keep the French from claiming New Holland, were more interested in drinking than keeping the peace. Rough justice would, no doubt, be meted out by the sealer's mates in due course.

Outside the building, the wind struck Anderson like a blow. He sucked greedily at the fresh air. His head felt light and his stomach churned as the recent intake of alcohol flooded through his system. The newly healed scar on his face ached with the cold. Stumbling a little in the unfamiliar terrain, he moved instinctively towards the beach. The three Beetles from the *Vigilant* were there, tilted on their sides, their oars stowed and resting in their rowlocks. Anderson's first thought was to head west. But with the crosswind blowing it would be difficult to manoeuvre the unwieldy whaleboat. It was designed for four men to row and one to steer. He would have to raise the mast and sail to manage her on his own. It would be quicker to run before the wind, around the headland and into the next bay to the east. He didn't know how far away that would be. He had no supplies, no water. And he needed rest, to clear his head. Always more comfortable at sea than on land, he decided to sail with the wind.

Given his reputation, no one would believe that he had not intended to kill the man. What was it the sealer had said? 'A mug's game – whalin'.' Well, he was right there. And he certainly hadn't deserved to die for expressing his opinion. But nothing could bring him back now. Nothing could bring any of them back. Anderson lived with death as he did with the lice that infested his bedding. In his experience, human beings were expendable, in spite of what his father's Bible said. He felt the bulge of the book in his jacket. He had tried to throw it away once, in a fit of anger, but had gone back and retrieved it from the filthy alleyway of some forgotten port.

The idea occurred to him that, outlawed as he was at the bottom of the world, perhaps he could become his own man. The sea was his only home, but he had no desire to go back to the *Vigilant*. And no one would regret his departure. His crime had set him free.

Putting his massive shoulder to the stern of the nearest Beetle, he pushed and heaved it across the sand. At the water's edge, he lifted the mast and fitted it into its shoe. This made the vessel top heavy in the shallow water, but it would be impossible to raise the mast single-handed once he was underway. Finally, his heart pounding and his black skin shining with sweat, he pushed the boat into deeper water, scrambled aboard and grabbed the steering oar. With the familiar movement of the ocean beneath him once more, he immediately felt better.

Anderson hauled up the sail and it filled with wind. As the boat picked up speed, steering became easier. He settled himself with one hand on the stern oar, the sail rope in the other.

A half moon showed briefly between the scudding clouds, then disappeared again. But even without its light the solid blackness of the land stood out in sharp contrast to the shining water and paler sky. He reached the point, rounded it and followed the curve of the beach, standing out from the shore just far enough to keep wind in his sail and deep water beneath him.

A limestone cliff appeared. As Anderson got closer he saw that it was pitted with caves, their mouths yawning black against the grey stone. He decided to hide the boat in one of them.

After beaching the Beetle, it took all Anderson's strength to push and drag it across the narrow strip of sand to the mouth of a large cave. He concealed the boat by breaking off the branches from some scrubby bushes to cover the stern. From the mouth of the cave, he listened carefully for signs of life. The sea breathed in and out, but nothing else seemed to inhabit the blackness.

Anderson lowered his body to the dry, sandy floor beside the boat. He was bone weary. The privations of a year at sea, the injuries he had sustained, the shock of killing a man and the effort of sailing the Beetle single-handed had all combined to drain his strength. The alcohol that had burned down into his empty stomach and settled to create a pleasant warmth now made his head feel light and disconnected. But he could not afford to sleep. He must stay awake, alert to the dangers of an unfamiliar shore and angry men seeking revenge.

In the early hours of the morning, the wind died away. The resulting silence was intense. Anderson found it alien, but not unpleasant. Even riding at anchor, a ship is never silent. During the long watches of the night, when only the helmsman and the lookout are awake, there is still the sound of the rigging, the tick and rattle of rings and latches, the creak of the timbers and the lapping of the sea against the hull.

In spite of his resolve not to, he fell asleep. When he woke, his head was clearer. Every muscle of his body was stiff and aching, but that was the least of his problems. As the pale dawn began to steal across the entrance to his cave, Jack Anderson saw, with renewed clarity, that he would never return to the life he had known.

8

JOHN BATHURST BENT OVER THE BODY ON THE FLOOR OF THE PUB.

'Get the doctor!' he shouted, and pressed his ear to the man's chest.

'He's in his barracks,' the publican said, kneeling on the other side of the body.

'Well, get him here!' Bathurst demanded.

'No need,' the publican said. 'This one's already dead and gone.'

Bathurst sat back on his heels. Other men stood about awkwardly, shifting their feet, but seeming unable to leave the room.

'Bloody Anderson,' one of the *Vigilant* crewmen muttered.

'Told ya he'd got the devil in him,' another said, crossing himself.

'Who knows this man here?' John Bathurst asked, looking at the faces around him.

'He's a sealer.'

'Was a sealer,' the publican reminded them.

'Where's his mates?' Bathurst persisted.

'Don't know that he had mates.' Two men in sealskin coats

and rough woollen beanies looked at each other. 'But we're the ones what'll make sure no black bastard gets away with his murder.'

Thus reassured that something would be done, the men in the bar resumed their drinking while the publican and John Bathurst carried the dead man out to the back room where they laid him on a pile of empty sacks and covered him with a blanket.

'Doc'll see to him tomorrow,' the publican said. 'When he comes round.' Bathurst looked up sharply, but the publican gave a wry grin. 'Not him,' he said, indicating the man on the floor. 'The doc. He'll be sleepin' by now, with a flagon of brandy in him – as near as maybe.'

Next morning, as the sailors from the *Vigilant* began to rouse themselves from wherever they had fallen and wend their way down to the beach, a shout went up. One of their whaleboats was missing.

'I told you men to beach the boats with less haste and proper care!' Captain Carpo was none too pleased with what he assumed was just sloppy seamanship.

'It were well grounded, Cap'n,' the headsman claimed. 'I seen to it meself.'

'Damnation! Now we've lost a hand and a boat!'

'I reckon Anderson took it.'

'Don't be daft, man. Even he couldn't manage it on his own.' But the captain would later acknowledge that, in twenty years at sea, he had never known a man quite like Jack Anderson.

Word spread quickly. Anderson had taken a whaleboat.

But he wouldn't get far. If the sea didn't finish him off, the local sealers would. Like him, they were skilled seamen, but much more at home in the largely uncharted waters around King George Sound. They carried detailed maps of the area in their heads and could find their way between the hundreds of reefs and off-shore islands as easily as if they were taking an afternoon stroll. There was a lot of talk in the pub. Everyone present agreed to keep an eye out along the coast. But they were in no hurry. Confident they would catch up with him, one way or another, one enterprising sailor was even taking bets as to how far the big American would get before they did.

A grave was dug and the dead man buried. There was no priest in the settlement so Captain Carpo was called on to conduct the funeral. The *Vigilant* would not be ready to leave for at least two more days. Repairs were carried out during daylight hours, but after dark the sailors congregated in the pub, as before.

Later that night, when the noise in the bar was at its height, a bulky figure came up from the sea and stole silently into the settlement. The bars on the back window of the store were carefully unscrewed with a knife. The figure disappeared inside. When he emerged, he was carrying a bulging sack.

9

LOADED DOWN WITH FLOUR, SUGAR, LIQUOR AND A TINDERBOX, Anderson set off in an easterly direction. It was a long walk back, across country, to the bay where the whaleboat lay hidden. He had already spent the previous day lying low, thinking things through and deciding what to do. The first part of his plan had gone without a hitch. As he neared his destination, he began to relax and reflect on his situation.

Anderson knew that some of his former shipmates already called him a Jonah. Although it seemed illogical, by surviving certain death to finish off the job of killing the whale he had somehow increased their suspicions. They would now add murder to their list of his crimes. But worse than that, he had stolen one of their whaleboats which further reduced their ability to earn money from the voyage. And he had deserted his ship. His father would be ashamed.

Thinking about his father brought a lingering pain, a sadness and sense of loss that he must learn to live with, for he could never go back. Of all his crimes, it was this desertion that added most weight to the burden he carried. His heart was heavy and his shoulders sagged beneath the sack. But at no time did he think that life was not worth living.

Through all the hardships of his earlier years there was always an instinct for survival. It was still as strong in him as ever. Walking steadily back over the ground he had covered several hours earlier, that instinct began to tell him to pay more attention to his surroundings.

Something, besides himself, moved and breathed near by. He had noticed it before and dismissed it as a native animal of some sort. But it hadn't gone away.

Anderson changed direction, then changed again. These manoeuvres convinced him. Someone was following. He lowered the sack of stores to the ground. Unencumbered by his load, he circled around, keeping low and treading carefully.

He crouched even lower when the figure of a man came into view. Wearing a seaman's coat and a woollen hat pulled well down over his head, the man walked slowly in the half-dark, watching and listening.

Anderson decided that his best hope was to confront his pursuer. There were not many people who could match Anderson in size and strength. A blow to the head that rendered his stalker unconscious would be the best outcome. But having killed once, he would not hesitate to do it again.

The man paused to look around. Anderson chose this moment to rush him and bring him, struggling, to the ground.

'Avast and belay, you great ox!' The voice was that of John Bathurst.

'You!' Anderson declared, glaring angrily at the man beneath him. 'Of all men, I bin thinkin' you would maybe gain me some time, brother.'

'And you'd a bin right there,' Bathurst replied. 'But I be fixna change my mind any minute now, so let me up and listen, for I be havin' things to say to you.'

Anderson released him. 'I ain't goin' back,' he warned as Bathurst hitched his coat onto his shoulders and brushed himself down.

'I figured *that* out for maself,' he said.

Anderson studied him closely. 'You can be tellin' 'em from me, they ain't gonna take Jack Anderson alive!'

'You'll be needin' someone to watch yo' back.'

'I dunno . . .'

'I'm a-tellin' you,' Bathurst insisted. 'There's a bunch of sealers barkin' for yo' blood back there. Anyways, I'm fed up of whalin'. I reckon we can do better.'

Anderson sat down. Suddenly too weary to protest, he listened, without speaking, to what Bathurst had to say.

'You heard 'em in the bar. Whalin's a mug's game. A sealer done got more chance of makin' money. Good pelts sell for five shillin's *each*! And that trader back at the Sound, he can't get enough of 'em. Sells 'em in London for *two pounds* a piece! Cash money to the sealers, on the spot. And a lot easier than chasin' whales, man. So what you reckon, eh?'

Anderson had not thought beyond making himself a shelter, catching fish and raiding the alcohol supply at the settlement when he ran out of grog. Was Bathurst offering to throw in his lot with a murderer who had stolen a boat and deserted his ship? To join him and become an outcast, forever dodging the law and the other sealers in this godforsaken place? Besides, what did either of them know about sealing? Nothing.

'Seals is everywhere down here. Millions of 'em,' Bathurst was saying as if he had read Anderson's mind. 'You done got the boat, the oars an' sail. I got the crew.'

'What crew?' Anderson looked around, immediately on edge again. Was this some sort of trap? He and Bathurst had worked well together in close quarters and difficult conditions, but there was no one else from the *Vigilant* that Anderson was prepared to trust.

Without a sound, a man appeared not six feet away.

'Gimble,' he said, and held out his hand to Anderson.

Peering at him in the half light, Anderson recognised the man who had been sitting on the other side of the now-dead sealer.

'And why would you be joinin' up with the man who killed yo' mate?' Anderson demanded, full of suspicion.

'He ain't no mate of mine,' Gimble said firmly. 'I never seen any of 'em before. I'm just after sayin' t'anks, but no t'anks to the hospitality of His Majesty in Van Diemen's Land, if ya get me drift.'

'Says he be handy with the oars,' Bathurst said to the scowling Anderson while Gimble backed up this statement with a lengthy description of his escape from the penal colony. This entailed the daring theft and consequent rowing of an open boat across Bass Straight to Cape Howe with two other convicts from the notorious prison for repeat offenders at Macquarie Harbour.

Anderson took some convincing. But eventually he led both men to where he had abandoned the sack of provisions, and from there to the beach where the boat was hidden.

10

DURING THE FOLLOWING SUMMER, ANDERSON, BATHURST AND GIM-
ble developed into an efficient, close-knit team as they hunted
seals for meat and skins among the islands of the Recherche
Archipelago.

Named by the French explorer Baudin just over twenty
years before, the 105 islands of the Recherche lay scattered
like a handful of giant pebbles to the south and west of Cape
Arid. Some were little more than bare rocks rising straight
out of the sea, constantly battered by wind and waves. Others
had mineral-rich soil, vegetation and plentiful bird life.
Although they were all stripped bare by the pounding seas on
their western and southern shores, the northern and eastern
aspects of some of these islands offered sheltered coves and
sandy beaches.

At first the three men moved around, camping on a different island each night, sleeping in turns, watching and
listening for signs of pursuit. As well as seal meat, they ate
fish, shellfish and mutton-birds, and used their canvas sail
to collect rainwater until they got to know where permanent
springs and freshwater pools could be found.

As the days and weeks went by and they saw no other human being, they relaxed their vigilance. They no longer concealed the boat at night, but simply hauled it up onto the beach. In good weather, they slept under the stars, covered only by the sealskins that they had dried by stretching them across the boards on the bow. During the wild storms that soon began to pass through their chain of islands, they took shelter in limestone caves. Although it was a hard life, they were three like-minded men who relished the freedom of the open seas, the challenge of living off the land and the camaraderie of surviving against the odds. Many years later, Gimble would recall these as some of the best days of his adult life.

But, inevitably, their supply of alcohol ran out. They had skins to trade, but Anderson didn't want to risk arrest by going in to King George Sound. Instead of hiding from passing ships, they began to hail them, offering to trade skins for grog and food. Anderson did the talking. He could be very persuasive. He was also quick to hold his knife at the throat of any captain who refused his request. Bathurst then moved in and took what they needed. Gimble usually stayed with the boat, ready for a quick get-away, unless there was trouble and more man-power was needed on board.

Rumours of the giant black pirate and his small but effective crew spread quickly among the sealers, whalers and traders along the coast from the Sound to Kangaroo Island.

It wasn't long before ships became wary, keeping a better look out and trying to prevent this band of thieves from coming aboard. The pirates resorted to stealth again. The largely uncharted islands were dangerous to negotiate at night. But the three men now knew the coastline so well, they could fairly accurately predict which of the many bays a ship's captain would be likely to anchor in. When a ship was sighted from their camp on an island, they gauged its speed by wind and tide. Then, under cover of darkness, they would locate the ship and bring their whaleboat silently alongside. After jamming the ship's rudder, they would board her, bind and gag the watch and make their raid. Any opposition was dealt with in a swift and sometimes deadly manner. Their existence was close to the native animals they lived among and survival of the fittest was their only option. They were uncompromising men who expected to be treated in the same way by others. Once they had taken what they needed, the night-cloak of the ocean would quickly conceal them again.

It was during one of these raids that Anderson acquired two pistols and a quantity of shot. From that time on, he carried these pistols in his belt. Although he rarely fired them, the threat they posed in his hands was enough to gain the cooperation of most men.

The pirates were feared and hated, but not by everyone. Anger over the death of the sealer at King George Sound soon cooled. The demand for sealskins was far outstripping supply. Anderson and his men brought much-needed trade to the general store in the fledgling settlement and, although most people were aware of their crimes, there were more important things, like day-to-day survival, to preoccupy the locals. Some even looked forward to the visits of these colourful, if dangerous, characters, for they brought some relief from the tedium of everyday life in such a small and extremely isolated community.

'Anderson, isn't it?' The question came from a new arrival in the pub at Albany. Black Jack quickly took in the man's grubby woollen beanie, his calloused hands and frayed trousers. But it was the eyes, bloodshot and not quite aligned with each other, that worried Anderson most.

'Who's askin'?' he demanded.

'I could give yuz a name, but it would be one of many,' the man said. 'I was thinkin' another hand would be more use to ya.'

'We manage,' Anderson replied.

'Sure ya do.' The man raised his tankard in acknowledgement. 'But I'm handy with a knife.' In a flash the weapon appeared in his hand. He paused to gauge the effect of this demonstration. Then a crooked smile passed across his face. 'On the skins of course,' he added, slicing the air with his blade. 'Clean as a whistle and worth twice the price when Henry Paine gives 'em the treatment.'

Bathurst and Gimble examined the man with interest. The tedious process of removing the fat from the sealskins, without damaging the fur, was the thing they hated most. It required so much more precision than the broad sweeps of the scythes that Anderson and Bathurst were used to when carving up a whale carcass. Gimble usually performed the task, but he wasn't very good at it. On the other hand, could this Henry Paine be trusted?

Living by their wits in such precarious circumstances,

they had to be careful. Anderson and Bathurst, both African-Americans who had grown up in Massachusetts, were also linked by their *Vigilant* experience. Once they stepped outside the law, Anderson's size and skill with words gave authority to Bathurst's softer voice and smaller stature, while Bathurst's patience and native cunning got Anderson out of many a tricky situation when the bigger man's quick temper and instinct to fight, no matter how heavily the odds were stacked against them, could easily have seen them both killed.

Gimble was, in some ways, the odd man out. He had been accepted because of his sealing and rowing skills and because the Beetle was much easier to manage with three hands than with two. The situation suited him. He could stay out of reach of the law while building up a small fortune, since everything was shared equally between the three men. If they agreed to take on Paine, then it would be a four-way split. Anderson would insist on that.

Meanwhile, Paine seemed to have forgotten his offer. He had turned away from Anderson and was drinking and swapping stories with another man at the bar. An hour later, however, when the pub had closed and the three pirates were returning to their boat for the night, Henry Paine was suddenly there beside them. Anderson's hand went instinctively to his own knife.

'Well, whadaya say?' Paine asked, raising his empty hands above his head to prevent any misunderstanding.

'Escaped? Or done yo' time?' Bathurst asked.

'Arr well, I've a price on me head, 'tis true, but then you fellers ain't exactly dinin' with the magistrate, are ya now?'

'We take no passengers,' Anderson told him.

'I'm no blood-suckin' leech! I have skills to trade, fair and square,' Paine declared.

'There ain't gonna be no treachery.' Bathurst's voice was quiet, but menacing.

'I swear on me mother's life,' the man said solemnly, using one finger to make a rough cross over his heart. 'Assumin' of course that she ain't dead yet. Besides, if I scuppered youse jolly gent'amen I'd be in mortal danger of goin' down with the ship, would I not?'

Anderson paused to consider this. Then, with one nod of the head, Paine was accepted.

Henry Paine was one of many who came and went from Anderson's crew. Some were ex-convicts, some ticket-of-leave men who found life within the law too difficult to sustain. Others were adventurers, simply looking for a way to make a quick fortune. The ones who left because of ill health or injury were threatened and sworn to secrecy. Those who left without Anderson's blessing were rarely seen or heard of again.

11

WAVES SLAPPED GENTLY AGAINST THE HULL OF A SCHOONER RIDING at anchor in the shelter of a bay on the edge of the Great Australian Bight. Lamps burned brightly in her cabins fore and aft and voices, raised in laughter, drifted out into the night.

Apart from the crewman on watch, there was no one above decks when Anderson and his men came quietly in under her stern. With a wedge of wood, specially cut for the purpose, the ship's rudder was jammed and the smaller boat slid alongside. Under cover of darkness, three men scaled her ropes.

Nimble Gimble captured the watchman, holding a silencing hand over his mouth and a knife at his throat. Anderson and Bathurst went below. Avoiding the captain's quarters with its jolly sounds of a meal being consumed, they let themselves into the passengers' cabins. Having rifled through the luggage and pocketed anything of value, they separated to carry out the rest of their plan. Bathurst guarded the hatch, effectively locking the crew in below, while Anderson flung open the door to the captain's quarters.

'We've no gold on board!' the captain declared. Although he

had never seen Anderson, he was in no doubt about the identity of the huge black man who was blocking the doorway.

'That ain't what we bin hearin',' Anderson growled, brandishing a pistol in each hand. 'Give us the key to yo' chest.'

No one moved.

'There's nowt in it but clothing – personal effects,' the captain pleaded, while the first mate and four passengers sat in stunned silence around the table.

Anderson strode across the cabin and placed the pistol at the captain's head. 'Look lively or I'm gonna blow yo' brains out!'

'The key is in the drawer. I'll get it for you,' the mate said, rising from his seat.

'You stay right there,' Anderson ordered. Sidestepping around them, he opened the drawer. As he had suspected, there was a firearm inside, but the keys were there too. Shoving one pistol into his belt and keeping them all covered with the other, he picked up the keys and threw them to the captain.

'Open her up!' Anderson waved his pistol menacingly.

The captain glanced towards the open door. Muffled shouts and curses had begun to drift up from below. But Anderson was growing impatient and it was obvious to the captain that any help from that direction would arrive too late. Reluctantly, he opened the chest.

It was full of gold sovereigns. News of their 'secret' transportation from London to Van Diemen's Land in the schooner *Sea Flower* had filtered through to Anderson during the eight and a half months since the ship had left England. Formal communications were exasperatingly slow, but rumours and gossip spread with lightning speed between sailors who, after a few drinks in a foreign port, were often desperate to talk of home and to skite about what they knew.

Anderson scooped up coins and filled the canvas bag that hung from his belt. Still brandishing the pistol, he slung the bag over his shoulder, backed out through the door, and locked it behind him with a key that he had taken from the inside. He threw the key into the sea once he had no further use for it.

In a matter of minutes, the raiding party was back in the whaleboat with Henry Paine and Nimble Gimble pulling away from the disabled schooner while the bound and gagged watchman stared after them from the rail.

'Yo' captain be needin' you down below, man!' Anderson shouted, and his laughter echoed across the bay.

The pirates made for an island where their Beetle could be concealed. Although they were confident that there would be no pursuit, they posted a watch before they lit a fire and sat around it, counting out their new wealth. The gold was divided evenly among the four men. Anderson was scrupulous about every member of his crew receiving equal shares. He was well aware of the damage that could be caused by festering discontent, even among trusted men.

For over a year, the pirates continued to sail their open boat among the islands of the Recherche Archipelago. With Henry Paine now part of the crew, they killed seals, skinned them and cured the skins to produce top quality pelts. Sometimes they were able to trade these skins, for supplies or money, with passing ships. It was quicker and easier than making the journey to King George Sound. And they could relieve the ship's occupants of their valuables as well, if they were not happy with the terms of trade.

It was during the winter of 1828, when very few ships braved the fierce storms that regularly swept the area, that the pirates found the ever-increasing pile of skins taking up too much space in the whaleboat and their loaded money belts becoming heavy and awkward to carry.

'We need a bigger boat,' Henry Paine complained.

'We need a base camp,' Anderson countered.

Bathurst disagreed. 'Askin' for trouble,' he warned. 'A movin' target be harder to hit.'

But Anderson already had a plan.

One of the islands where they had spent several nights was larger and offered more protection than any of the others. It had good soil and vegetation. On their previous visit they had discovered a salt lake only a mile or so from the most sheltered bay. They had gathered salt from the shores of the lake and taken it with them for curing skins and salting fish.

This island also had a natural clearing in a hollow, hidden from the sea by a limestone ridge. A good stand of trees, unusually tall and thick for these barren windswept parts, offered shade and shelter.

A smaller island, named Goose Island by the pirates for its resident colony of Cape Barren Geese, sat squarely across the narrow entrance to the horseshoe-shaped bay, shielding it from prying eyes. Huge swells rolled all the way up from the Antarctic and smashed themselves to pieces against Goose

Island before arriving, tamed and submissive, in the bay itself. Only the bravest and most observant of sailors would venture close enough to discover the narrow passage into what later became known as Goose Island Bay.

Having noticed several granite outcrops on the island, Anderson felt sure that there would be fresh water. They landed and set about looking for a natural basin where the run-off from these rocks would be likely to collect. The men dug for several hours without success until finally, as Anderson had predicted, one hole quickly filled with fresh, cold drinking water. They shored up the sides of this hole with pieces of granite and fashioned a lid from the wood of the wattle trees that grew thickly near by.

For nearly a decade, Anderson and his fluctuating crew of pirates would be based on this island. Officially named *Ile du Millier* by the French explorer Baudin, the sealers called it Middle Island.

12

BY 1829, THE GROUP ON MIDDLE ISLAND HAD GROWN TO SIX MEN. During a visit to King George Sound, Frank Mead and Isaac Winterbourne, a pair of deserters from an English schooner, managed to persuade Anderson to let them join his crew. Bathurst was uneasy.

'More men means more mouths to feed,' he said. But Anderson had already weighed this up against the advantages. More men meant more seals and a larger raiding party. Get-away times would be faster with more men rowing. 'Yo' too trustin', man,' Bathurst complained.

'Yeah? Any man fool enough to mess with me will be lyin' down below – with fish feastin' on his eyeballs,' Anderson said vehemently.

To keep the men occupied, Anderson set them the task of building a more permanent dwelling. With no tools, other than their sealing knives, he and his men constructed a hut of fallen bush timber and granite rocks, both of which were plentiful on the island.

First, they built a large, communal room. Partly dry-stone walls, partly wattle and daub, the structure was finished off with thick, papery bark from melaleucas to make the roof more waterproof. They built an open fireplace into the wall at one end of the room. This served to heat the hut, and to cook their food. The windows had shutters, but no glass. Several hessian bags were opened out and sewn together to hang in the outer doorway.

All this purposeful activity was so effective in calming the men's tempers that, when the first room was finished, Anderson ordered a second one built. This he commandeered as his own personal quarters. Later, as he became more affluent, sealskins were sacrificed and sewn together to hang in the doorway between the communal area and his private room. Gradually, a storeroom and verandas were added until the hut became a substantial and relatively comfortable base for Anderson and his men.

The subject of women was one often bandied about among the isolated sailors, whose needs surfaced more regularly during idle times when they sat around the fire telling lurid stories of earlier sexual conquests.

As the pirates ranged eastwards across the Great Australian Bight, putting in to the mainland or Kangaroo Island, Anderson himself had taken advantage of the hospitality of local Aboriginal women. He found the Ngarrinda women particularly comely and greatly admired their ability to swim with the seals. Their fluid movements and wet, brown bodies made them almost indistinguishable from the sleek marine creatures as they herded selected animals ashore to be killed by their menfolk for meat and skins, always taking care not to jeopardise the continuity of the colony in the process.

These Aboriginal women, for their part, were fascinated by the huge black man, so like and yet unlike their own people. They watched, giggling as Anderson washed at their water-hole and shaved using his razor-sharp sealing knife.

It was during the second winter on Middle Island, with the hut finished and Anderson's leadership of the pirates well established, that he decided to make a more permanent arrangement with these native women.

On a morning when the sea was relatively calm and the winds had returned to a summer pattern, Anderson announced that he would take the boat to Kangaroo Island. In the past, he had used the island as a base, close to the mainland country of the women he preferred, but far enough away to escape pursuit, should that be nessessary. The crew quickly made their preparations.

Running before a strong south-westerly with their sail bulging and a pod of dolphins playing around their bow, the men headed across the Bight. Just before dark, a ship was sighted, flying the colours of His Majesty's Royal Navy. Anderson's reputation was now well known and ships planning to cross the Bight faced a dilemma. Their captains were warned not to hug the coast too closely as Anderson's boat was small enough to be easily concealed among the hundreds of inlets but fast enough to catch and board a three-master in the fickle off-shore winds. They were advised to take their courage in both hands and strike directly across the uncharted expanse of water. Even then, they would not be entirely safe, for Anderson was a formidable seaman and knew the Southern Ocean better than anyone. Ships would arrive in the ports of Albany or Hobart with their chests emptied of gold and silver coins, minus their food supplies, ropes, anchors or anything else that Anderson happened to need. He was by now a rich man. Conscious of the possibility that, sooner or later, he might have to buy his life at short notice, he had been amassing a small fortune. But the thrill of the chase – the lightning raid, the frantic run back to the safety of Middle Island – was hard for him to resist. And here was a ship, just asking to be raided. The women would have to wait.

Approaching the vessel just after dark, Anderson and his men came in under the stern of HMS *Shannon*, jammed her rudder and began scrambling up her ropes. But the captain had been looking out for them. He had orders to capture Anderson if he came within range, and take him to Hobart for trial.

At pistol point, the captain called on Anderson to surrender. The raid was abandoned. Shots were fired and Anderson sustained a flesh wound to the shoulder as he and Gimble fought their way to the rail. They both managed to leap into the waiting Beetle and the others pulled on the oars.

The pirates kept their whaleboat in close to the hull, making use of the deeper shadows thrown by the towering ship and the fact that the Navy marksmen would be hard pressed to hit Anderson's boat without damaging their own. Ignoring the blood running down his arm, Anderson took control of the steering oar. With her full crew now in place, the Beetle left the uncertain protection of the hull and headed for the open sea.

But the captain of the *Shannon* was determined to take the

big American alive and the ship's own whaleboat was, even then, being launched to give chase.

With the swells running high ahead of a southerly buster, the pirates bent their backs to the oars. There was no time to hoist their sail and no real advantage to be gained by tacking into the howling wind. But with only four oarsmen to do the pulling, the Beetle was being overtaken by the *Shannon's* larger, six-man boat.

In a direct line between Anderson and safety lay the twin islands of Hastler and Helby. These rocky outcrops towered sixty to eighty feet straight out of the sea and were separated by a narrow channel. Anderson had sailed around them many times. But the other boat was closing in and would fire on the Beetle again, if it could get within range. With his men visibly tiring, he heaved on the steering oar and pointed the bow straight at the narrow gap between the rocks.

Even in flat, calm conditions, to take a whaleboat with a six-and-a-half-foot beam through that slim gap would be difficult. In a high swell with waves beating against the cliffs sending up curtains of blinding spray and the undertow sucking huge quantities of water back from the entrance, it looked impossible.

Although they trusted Anderson's seamanship, when the crew saw what he intended every man's face showed disbelief.

'Pull!' Anderson roared, knowing they must not hesitate. 'Pull, for the devil himself is waitin' down below!'

They pulled.

With arms and shoulders bulging, chins tucked in and backs arched, they heaved against the waves.

The Beetle rode up and paused high on the swell. One set of oars flailed uselessly. The undertow sucked like a plug-hole below them and the sheer rocks on either side threw back a stinging spray. Hanging in mid-air for what seemed like a lifetime, every man on board began to pray to his maker – except Anderson.

He stood calmly in the stern, a half-smile on his face. The wave collapsed and dropped the boat with a bone-jarring crash that shook her from stem to stern. The steering oar bucked and flew, rebellious, even in Anderson's huge hands. He held on in spite of his injured shoulder while the men pulled for dear life, adrenalin pumping in their veins. The next swell carried their battered boat through to the relative calm between the rocks.

Cheers went up. Men shouted and laughed with relief. Their voices bounced off the cliffs that walled them in on either side. Looking back to the entrance, they caught a glimpse of the *Shannon*'s whaleboat turning away. But they were not safe yet.

'Bravo, my lusty rogues!' Anderson cried, in a rare moment of congratulation. 'Rattle them ro'locks and pull for home, now. We ain't got a minute to spare for I wager the Jack Tars will be thinkin' to meet us on the other side.'

Feeling elated, even invincible, the crew pulled with new energy. Between the sheltering cliffs, the surface of the mile-long channel was calm. But a strong current rushed beneath their boat, pushing them towards the boiling cauldron of wind and swell at the other end as if, having failed to swallow them, the sea was now trying to spit them out. Men and boat took another battering and came within a hair's breadth of being dashed to pieces on the rocks before they finally emerged into the open sea. Middle Island was within reach and His Majesty's Navy nowhere to be seen.

13

ALMOST A MONTH LATER, ON A CLEAR AUTUMN DAY, A YOUNG MAN called James Manning was working along the rows of radishes and cabbages in a small, cleared patch of ground on Kangaroo Island. Catching sight of something in the distance, he stopped weeding and stood squinting out over the white-capped waters of the bay.

A boat was approaching.

It came out of the west, running before the wind with its single sail billowing and the imposing figure of Black Jack Anderson standing in the stern. The sun shone on Anderson's bare head and arms. His solid legs, astride the transom, were encased in long sealskin boots and a full-length fur cape hung from his broad shoulders.

Manning himself still wore the fraying remains of a Sydney suit, the trousers now held up with a twist of cord made from the stringy island grass. With the buttons long gone, his jacket was laced tight against the cold by a string of the same grass, threaded through the buttonholes.

'Them spuds will not be helped to grow by you standin' there like a scarecrow,' Captain Merredith complained as he puffed up the hill to join Manning. When he saw who was visiting, the captain's face paled. But James Manning dropped his makeshift hoe and raced towards the beach, leaping and sliding down the sandy path.

For almost two years, James Manning had been marooned on Kangaroo Island with Captain Merredith, another passenger, John Griffiths, and Merredith's wife, Mai, after their ship, the *Defiance*, was wrecked.

Mai came from the Kilcarer-Gundidj Aboriginal people whose lands covered the south-west coast of Victoria. Her life had never been easy and the wreck of the *Defiance* was not Mai's first brush with death. Traditionally, Kilcarer-Gundidj mothers breastfed their offspring until they were four or five years old. Any subsequent babies born within that time were allowed to die, since the mother could not provide for more than one at a time. As her mother's second child, born just thirteen months after her sister, Mai had been lucky to be adopted by an aunt whose own baby was stillborn. But she was never quite accepted by either of her 'fathers'. It was their shared belief that she should be married off as soon as possible. The spirited and resourceful Mai had other ideas. In love with someone else, she refused to marry the old man to whom she had been promised, and fled to avoid the punishment that would inevitably be carried out by her own people.

On one of his many voyages around the south and east coasts of Australia, Merredith had put ashore to repair his ship, which had suffered some damage in a storm. He had come upon Mai, cold, emaciated and hungry, sheltering alone in a beach cave. Merredith had found the girl attractive with her wild hair and even wilder eyes. And she was obviously in awe of him, probably thinking he was one of the spirit people who seemed to be coming more and more frequently out of the sea. Merredith managed to calm Mai's fears. He wrapped her in his coat and brought her back to the *Defiance*.

His crew at the time was not happy about having a woman on board. Any stranger aboard a ship was considered bad luck, but a woman was particularly suspect. Mai, however, soon won them over. With her slender limbs and smooth polished skin, she was a pleasant sight for men long deprived of the company of women. And, once she got used to the ship's galley, she proved to be very hard working. As well as her more private duties in the captain's cabin, she cooked, cleaned and washed for all the men. Merredith made it clear that he would kill anyone who so much as laid a finger on her lustrous brown body. And it seemed that, having accepted his protection, she was prepared to do anything to please the captain. Unfortunately, on its very next voyage and with James Manning on board, the *Defiance* was wrecked, confirming the superstitious beliefs of the crew.

Manning had paid for his passage to Swan River Colony, where better opportunities were to be had, or so he was told. The best land around Sydney Cove had already been taken up, so the ambitious young man had decided that the new colony was where his fortune would be made.

When the *Defiance* was wrecked, on Cape Howe Island, Manning was thrown into the sea. Huge waves closed over him. He felt himself dragged deeper into darkness and thought his lungs would burst and his life would be over, since he could not swim. But somehow his thrashing limbs brought him to the surface, close enough for the crew to drag him, gasping and vomiting sea water, into one of the two small boats that they had managed to launch from the deck of the sinking ship.

Three crewmen were lost. The remainder were sent back, in one of the lifeboats, to Botany Bay. Captain Merredith, however, had felt a responsibility towards his two paying passengers, James Manning and John Griffiths. The captain was adamant that they could reach their destination on the other side of the continent in the whaleboat, which was the more seaworthy of the small open boats salvaged from the wreck. The two boats sailed away in opposite directions.

After several arduous months at sea, battling the elements, never knowing where or when they would next find food and water, Captain Merredith, Mai and his two passengers arrived at Kangaroo Island. They were exhausted, dehydrated and near starvation. What supplies they had managed to salvage from the *Defiance* had run out. They had survived on fish, when they could catch them, and occasionally seal meat. Fresh water was always a problem as they were dependent on what rain they could collect in their canvas buckets.

Since he had come this far in the name of honouring his promise to his paying passengers, no one expected the eccentric Captain Merredith to suddenly declare that he would go no further.

'Here we have beautiful rich soil, abundant wildlife, a wonderful climate and everything is free – there is nowhere on earth closer to paradise than this. Believe me, for I have sailed all the seven seas,' he proclaimed.

'But you promised . . .' The young James Manning did not share the captain's view of the small, scrubby island with no real shops, roads or pubs and virtually no company, apart from the dour John Griffiths who, at forty-five, was much closer to Merredith in age.

'There will be ships, lad. No doubt you will be able to work your passage on one of them,' Merredith told Manning before stomping off and refusing to discuss the matter further.

In desperation, the young man thought of stealing the whaleboat. But he was no sailor and knew he could never manage such a voyage on his own. He began to see that his only hope of ever reaching the Swan River Colony was to be taken on board a passing ship. But although they sometimes saw ships in the distance, none had come close enough to hail.

Nineteen long months would pass before Black Jack Anderson came sailing into the bay.

The vessel resting on the beach was not exactly the ship Manning had imagined, but it was obviously seaworthy and not just passing through. It had landed on his doorstep. Manning felt that, at last, his luck had turned.

'Ahoy!' he shouted, and waved as Gimble and Paine leapt out of the Beetle into ankle-deep water and guided her onto the sand. Anderson stepped ashore, his cape swinging aside to reveal the two pistols shoved into the leather belt at his waist.

'James Manning,' the eager youth introduced himself, holding out his hand. Anderson regarded him coolly for several seconds before stretching out his own huge hand. Their calloused palms met briefly, before Anderson turned away without a word and climbed towards the garden. Manning followed, running to keep up.

Unable to match the giant's strides, Manning paused to catch his breath. The rest of the crew, having furled the sail, lowered the mast and stowed the oars, were also making their way up the path.

'I'm James Manning,' he tried again, this time holding out his hand to Isaac Winterbourne.

'So I heard,' Winterbourne said and he brushed past Manning to stride on up the steep path.

'Pay him no mind, lad,' Gimble said. His scarred face was split by a grin that showed the remains of black and broken teeth.

'Where you from?' James Manning asked. The sailor threw back his head and roared with laughter.

'Hark at him, Bathurst?' he called over his shoulder to the smaller of the two African-Americans. 'Rattle me ro'locks if this ain't the only soul left in the Southern Ocean what don't have us in his sights!'

'Aye, well let's hope he don't live to regret it.'

'Avast and belay. Ya'll be scarin' the lad,' Gimble laughed again. 'Sure we're just after enjoyin' ourselves. Bit of a holiday, ya might say. Courtesy of the boss, Black Jack Anderson.' Still grinning, he continued on up the path.

14

WHEN BLACK JACK ANDERSON LANDED ON KANGAROO ISLAND THAT
day, James Manning saw him as his saviour. But the ragged
youth's presence barely registered with Anderson. He had
come for one reason only – women.

The presence of Merredith's party on an otherwise unin-
habited part of the island was a surprise, but did not distract
Anderson from his purpose. It soon became clear that the paths
of the two men had crossed before. Mai, however, had not been
with Merredith then. She became the topic of animated conversation as Merredith emphatically established his prior claim
to her and Anderson assured the captain that his interests lay
elsewhere.

It was obvious that there was no love lost between Anderson and Merredith. But the unwritten law of the sea meant
that Anderson and his men must be allowed to repair their
boat, hunt and fish and generally be given shelter.

Mai cooked for them. While his crew ogled her and made
surreptitious approaches, Anderson remained aloof, standing off to one side and watching or sitting, drinking and
arguing with Merredith. But everyone was aware of him.

James Manning woke the next day feeling light and excited. At last he could leave this dead-end place. He saw his dream of becoming a landowner in the Swan River Colony once again within reach. For two years he had planned how it would be. He would arrive, make himself known to the authorities, claim his dues as a free settler and begin to farm his own land. It would be hard work, but he was young and strong. With the forty pounds he had managed to save he would hire help. He would grow crops and sell them for huge profits, buy sheep and sell the wool and meat. He had seen how the squatters and landowners in New South Wales prospered and became fat. He had even worked for some of them. In fact, it was his last employer who had told him about the opportunities opening up in the west.

Manning leapt up off his native-grass bed. He was ready to go. He had no bags to pack. His precious forty pounds were safely stitched into the lining of his jacket. He could not have been happier. He ran past the sailors' camp and up to the top of the hill.

There he stopped dead. The boat was gone.

Two days later, the Beetle returned. On board were Black Jack Anderson, John Bathurst and two Aboriginal women. The rest of the crew had stayed behind while Bathurst and Anderson made the short crossing to carry out their transaction on the mainland.

As they came ashore, the two women shyly averted their eyes. They were not bound and, when they did look up to examine their surroundings, they seemed more curious than fearful. Anderson looked pleased with himself, striding up the beach with more swagger than usual in his step.

John Bathurst, on the other hand, was furious. Glowering as darkly as the approaching storm clouds, he secured the boat and, while the women followed Anderson to the settlement inland, Bathurst strode along the beach to the farthest point, where he climbed up and sat, staring out to sea, avoiding his longtime friend and accomplice. When the storm broke, fierce winds and pelting rain eventually drove Bathurst down to the shelter of the settlement. But his relationship with Anderson would never be the same again.

There were no questions asked around the cooking fires that night. Bathurst sat, sullenly silent. Everyone knew better than to try and get the story from Anderson. He did not take kindly to being interrogated. But gradually, from the two men's actions over several days and a few overheard words, the situation became clear.

Anderson and Bathurst had been welcomed as guests by the local Ngarrinda people. Goods were exchanged for two young women, who knew how to herd seals and cure skins. But somehow, negotiations with the Ngarrindjeri elders had gone horribly wrong. Anderson had lost his temper, knocked two of their men unconscious and fired his pistols over the heads of the others. Then, in spite of Bathurst's protests, he had grabbed the two women from the fleeing group and carried them off.

The women struggled at first, then became resigned to their fate. The kidnapping of a woman was not unknown among their own people and they began to regard the whole episode as something of an adventure.

Hours later, back on Kangaroo Island, Bathurst was still admonishing Anderson for his barbaric behaviour. He feared that the Aborigines would now be set against them and looking for revenge, but more importantly he felt that Anderson had breached his own code of conduct. While women could be bought and even tricked or coerced into providing sexual favours, taking them by force was not condoned.

Anderson, on the other hand, acknowledged that he had lost his temper, but felt that he had only taken what was rightfully his.

'Have done with yo' jawin',' Anderson said impatiently. 'They ain't made no objections.' He indicated the two women who were, by then, engaging in animated communication with Mai.

'It don't do you no credit, for all that,' Bathurst insisted moodily.

Presently, with much laughing and arm-waving, Mai revealed that the women's names were Nurla and Bidjara, known as Biddi, and that they were unmarried. Their fathers and uncles were very angry, she said, but would never take the women back, now that they had been with Anderson. It would be impossible, under tribal law, for them to marry.

'They say big man lie with them. Now they belong him,' Mai pronounced.

'What will their relatives do?' Merredith asked her.

After consulting the women, Mai explained that Nurla and Biddi's people had no boat capable of following the kidnappers, but that their families would be suspicious of strangers and much more aggressive in the future. Anderson gathered his crew and prepared to depart immediately for Middle Island.

While the men put out their camp fire and dismantled their shelters, James Manning pleaded with Anderson.

'I am fit and strong. I will work hard and cause you no trouble. Take me only as far as King George Sound. I will make my own way to Swan River Colony from there.'

'A pow'ful long journey,' Anderson told him. 'Besides, we've a full complement.'

'But no relief,' Manning said. 'With you in the stern, there are only four men.'

'And two women,' Anderson reminded him.

'These women know nothing of boats,' Manning said dismissively. 'They are swimmers, whereas I am an experienced oarsman.' The young man drew himself up, trying to look taller, stronger. Anderson regarded him through slitted eyes. Then, with a slight shrug of his shoulders, he turned away.

'Does that mean you will take me?' Manning asked.

Anderson crossed the beach to where the boat was waiting. Manning ran behind him and scrambled in before the big American could change his mind. Lifting an oar from the bottom of the boat, Manning placed it in a forward rowlock and sat down on the thwart. Nurla and Biddi sat together in the bow. Anderson took up his position at the stern, towering over the steering oar. Nimble Gimble and Henry Paine shoved the whaleboat off from the beach and stepped aboard, pulling on the ropes to raise the sail before taking up their oars. John Bathurst, his face set in a mask of discontent, sat beside Manning. For a moment, he looked as if he was about to speak, but evidently changed his mind, bending his body to his oar instead.

As the boat glided away from Kangaroo Island, James Manning looked back at the figure of Captain Merredith, standing alone in his sloping garden above the beach.

'Paradise?' Manning grunted, 'He's welcome to it!' Turning his face to the ocean, he pulled with the rest.

Hugging the coast, flying before the easterly gales, rowing and tacking when the winds howled from the west, the group made their way back towards Middle Island.

On the fifth day, they spotted the *Mountaineer* hove-to in a sheltered bay. She was registered in Mauritius and regularly carried cargo, mail and sometimes gold and silver coins to Van Diemen's Land. Under sail, the Beetle passed by and both crews waved and shouted their greetings across the water. Anderson took the whaleboat around behind the nearest rocky island and put a bewildered Manning and the two women ashore.

'Where are you going? You can't leave us here!' Manning shouted, suspecting that they were being abandoned.

'Whist, lad,' Gimble reassured him. 'Sure we'll not be gone long.' Laughing among themselves, Anderson and his crew rowed quietly back to the ship. Just on dark, they jammed her rudder and boarded her. The skilled pirates had no trouble holding up the drunken captain, one Evanson Jansen, forcing him to hand over three flagons of brandy and all the coins he had in a seachest in his cabin. They then snatched a few supplies from the galley and disappeared swiftly and silently into the night.

An hour or so later, they returned to the tiny island and lit a small fire in a concealed corner of the beach. While Nurla and Biddi cooked the crabs they had gathered, all the loot was pooled and divided equally among the men who had gone with Anderson.

'Why was I not included?' Manning demanded.

'You agreed to work for your keep, boy,' Anderson growled. 'Nothin' more, nothin' less.'

'But you *will* take me to King George Sound.'

'Aye,' the big man said, crushing a crab claw between his teeth as if it was made of spun sugar. 'When next I go.'

After making sure that no one was holding anything back, Anderson took exactly the same share as the others. When it came to the two women, however, there were different rules. They belonged to Anderson and woe betide anyone who tried to take advantage of their presence.

15

A SUMMER STORM BLEW UP AND DELAYED THE BEETLE FURTHER. For two more days they battled huge swells. The boat was often carried up thirty feet or more before sliding down into a trough that obliterated the horizon for minutes at a time. There were periods when they could neither sail nor row and had to bail out water just to stay afloat. But Anderson, standing day after day at the steering oar in the stern of the boat like a statue carved from ebony, looked as if he could have gone on for ever. Riding the waves with his chin thrust forward and eyes like slits to minimise the glare, he noted and responded to every variation of wind or tide or swell. Under sail, he could transform the cumbersome boat into a racing yacht. When the wind died and the men were forced to row, Anderson steered the Beetle expertly through the seas to get the best out of boat and crew. At night they took shelter, as best they could, on any island that allowed them to land.

The ten-day journey had taken its toll. Even the hardened sailors were weary. James Manning and the Aboriginal women had suffered most from cold and seasickness. They lay in the bottom of the boat or hung over the gunwale, miserably heaving their hearts up into the sea.

Even so, it was with a great deal of whooping and hollering that the sailors dragged their battered craft up onto the beach in Goose Island Bay.

'Land ho, me hearty,' the ever-cheerful Nimble Gimble proclaimed to James Manning, who was hanging, limp and exhausted, over the side. 'Home sweet home – if she's not been laid flat by that there storm.'

With the oars stowed and the boat secured, the party straggled over the ridge to the hut in the centre of the island. There they were greeted by Johnno.

Johnno was a damaged young man Anderson had rescued from a rocky outcrop in the middle of the ocean where his former crewmates had abandoned him.

Taken on as a foremast hand for a voyage across the bottom of the world, the unfortunate young man was subject to fits. He would fall down, his body jerking and strange guttural sounds erupting from his frothing mouth. His shipmates had apparently thought him possessed of some sort of demon and had put him ashore at the first opportunity, promising to pick him up on their return. They never came back.

With nothing but the resident penguins to eat for over a year, Johnno had become increasingly deranged by solitude and malnutrition. Indeed he had presented a fearsome sight when Anderson and his men had first seen him standing on the top of his remote island. Part man, part mountain goat, with long matted hair covering much of his emaciated body, his eyes rolled wildly as the sealers approached. In spite of the fear and loathing loudly expressed by all of his crew at the time, Anderson had insisted on taking the whaleboat in close enough to land on the dangerously rocky shore.

The frightened castaway had not been easy to rescue. His speech was almost unintelligible from lack of use. He had run, screeching like a monkey, when the big black man had approached him. Anderson had tried to talk to him, but in the end had simply picked up the struggling Johnno and carried him, sliding the last few yards down the rock with the skeletal waif clasped firmly in his huge arms. Gimble and Paine had steadied the pitching boat as best they could while Bathurst had leaned out and dragged both rescuer and rescued aboard.

After several months on Middle Island, Johnno's health began to improve, but there were rumblings among the men about the extra mouth they were expected to feed. It was hard enough to keep body and soul together when everyone pulled their weight, they complained. But Anderson was adamant that no one was to lay a finger on Johnno and that he be given as much food as he needed. To pacify the men, he had a separate tent erected on the edge of the clearing for Johnno, who continued to have terrible nightmares. His fits, although less frequent, persisted. On one occasion, when Anderson caught Nimble Gimble capering around the clearing, mimicking Johnno's unusual gait while the others roared with laughter, he threatened them all with a pistol whipping.

'Arr, we don't mean nothin' by it. A bit of fun is all,' Gimble tried to explain.

'Enough!' Anderson raged. 'You don't mock no man who survives against such odds!'

Gimble was taken aback at the time and grumbled to the others, but later, recalling the stories of Anderson's earlier life, he came to understand that the big American, for all his ruthlessness, had great respect for survivors.

There was no more teasing of Johnno, at least not when Anderson was around. As the castaway slowly recovered his physical strength, he began to take his destiny into his own hands. Obviously fascinated by Nimble Gimble, he started to follow him everywhere. Before long, Johnno's own sense of humour asserted itself. He saw that he could turn his disabilities into an asset and began to entertain the men. Rolling his eyes and exaggerating his halting speech, he performed a range of antics to make them laugh.

'Come on, Johnno, give us a turn,' became a commonly heard request in the hut after the evening meal. Eventually, Johnno persuaded Gimble to lend him the tin whistle that the Irishman played occasionally. Gimble's repertoire consisted of sea shanties and a few Irish folk songs. But in Johnno's hands, the whistle produced bird calls, haunting, original melodies and lively dance tunes that, at the very least, set the men's feet tapping and often resulted in a full-blown hornpipe. The drunken sailors leaped about, laughing and falling down. Sometimes they got up again, but quite often they stayed where they fell to sleep off their skinful of alcohol. Anderson did not dance, but lounged against the veranda post, watching. There were no more mutterings about Johnno not pulling his weight.

Within days of his arrival on Middle Island, Manning went out with the sealers. But he was not a natural sailor. His stomach was never quite at ease with the motion of the boat. He hated being constantly wet, cold and covered in fish guts. His clothes began to smell of blood and entrails, in spite of the most fastidious washing in both sea and fresh water. The sealers taunted him mercilessly and gave him the added chore of carrying buckets of water from the well to the hut. 'Sure a washerwoman would be used to that,' they laughed.

Conscious of how much he now depended on these men, Manning said nothing, but he seethed inside. With Merredith he had felt frustrated and angry about what he had seen as a betrayal of trust. Here, among the drunken, violent sealers, he feared for his life.

Tightly packed bundles of thick grey cloud filled up the sky. Low swells and still autumn days had made the leaden sea look solid enough to walk on. Only the splashes of pale turquoise that lapped the beach warned that it was not what it seemed.

But long before winter set in, the winds of change had begun to blow through the clearing on Middle Island. Anderson felt their disturbing presence. He set the men to repairing the boat, patching holes that had appeared in the wattle-and-daub walls and roof of the hut and mending the shutters, fallen into disrepair over summer. In spite of this flurry of activity, he could not shake off the sombre mood. Since their return from Kangaroo Island, Bathurst had begun to talk of leaving, of going back to America.

'My bones be growin' weary,' he told his friend, who was younger by at least ten years.

'Arr, hark at the old man,' Anderson teased, appealing to the others for help in his attempt to jolly Bathurst into changing his mind. 'It be a rockin' chair we must build for him now?'

Bathurst grinned and raised his mug of rum to Anderson, but later, when most of the others had retired to their bed-rolls, the two men stood side by side warming themselves at the fire.

'I mean it, brother,' Bathurst said. 'I done had my fill of adventure. I'm fixna buy land, build me a house, see things grown, not destroyed.' Anderson turned his head away as if he didn't wish to hear, or perhaps to hide an unaccustomed emotion. 'I've gold aplenty . . . same as you,' Bathurst contin-ued. 'Come with me.'

'I can't go back,' Anderson said quietly.

The subject was not discussed again. But a Yankee whaler was sighted, passing through the archipelago. When it anchored in one of the Cape Arid bays, Bathurst strapped his money to his body and packed his bedroll.

'We bin good mates, you and me,' he said to Anderson.

'Aye, we have that.' Both men stood awkwardly for a moment before Anderson wrapped his arms around Bathurst, bear-like, and held him in a rough embrace. 'Fair winds and a straight wake to you now.'

Gimble and Paine delivered Bathurst to the ship's side and slipped away as quickly as they would from a raid. By morn-ing, the whaler was gone and Bathurst with it.

16

IF JAMES MANNING'S PERCEPTIONS HAD BEEN QUICKER, HE MIGHT have gone with Bathurst – even though the ship was sailing in the wrong direction. He had been desperate to escape the remote and isolated Kangaroo Island, but Middle Island was even worse. It was smaller, the soil was poor and there were very few edible berries and grasses. He even began to miss Captain Merredith's garden which, although he had always spoken of it in the most derogatory terms, had at least provided some variety in their diet. Nurla and Biddi had taken over the cooking and Manning suggested they cultivate the native sweet potato. He also experimented with the growing of various other edible plants.

Anderson had installed the two women in a camp of their own, in a separate clearing beyond the well. With Manning's help, they built a brushwood fence to keep out the wallaby-like tammars that continually scratched at the garden beds, uprooting and eating the young plants. Nurla and Biddi propagated yams and beets under Manning's instructions. Although he had complained loud and long about having to dig like a dog for edible roots and tend the potatoes in Merredith's garden, his skills proved invaluable on Middle Island, but even this was a constant struggle in the harsh conditions. As the weather improved he questioned Anderson about when his next trip to King George Sound would be.

'When I'm ready,' Anderson told him bluntly.

It became increasingly clear that, with good weather for sealing and an increasing number of passing ships to raid for provisions, ammunition and valuables, Anderson preferred to stay within his own domain. Manning resigned himself to a long stay on Middle Island with the thought he he could perhaps add to his precious forty pounds by going with the pirates on their raids.

In King George Sound, there had also been many changes. Since Anderson's previous visit, Sir Richard Spencer had arrived, with his family and his extensive household, to take up the post of Government Resident. By March 1835, the struggling town of Albany was beginning to show signs of permanence.

On the hill above the harbour, sixteen-year-old Jimmy Newell came bursting in to the crude two-room hut that housed his family. There were ten of them now crowded together under the one carefully thatched roof. Jimmy's father, James, a roof thatcher by trade, had emigrated from Sussex almost two years before with his wife, Hannah, and their seven surviving children. And recently, Jimmy's sister Mary had married, and her husband, Matthew Gill, had moved in with them.

'There's a ship in the harbour!' Jimmy announced with great excitement.

Caroline and Charles paused briefly, glanced up at their older brother, then continued the rough-and-tumble game they were playing on the floor. The baby, William, stirred in his handmade cot in the corner of the room, but didn't wake.

'And where else would a ship be?' Jimmy's sister Dorothy asked, tucking a long, damp strand of hair behind her ear before bending again over the seemingly endless mending in her lap.

'Not in the High Street, I hope.' Mary giggled, lifting her heavy skirt and petticoat to fan her legs.

'Course not!' Jimmy refused to let the sarcasm of his sisters dampen his enthusiasm. 'A real smart cutter, it is. And the captain's offerin' cheap passage to Van Diemen's Land. He says there's work to be had there. Fortunes to be made!' Jimmy looked directly at Matthew, hoping for his support.

'And this captain wouldn't be set on linin' his own pockets, I suppose?'

Dorothy, being the eldest, could remember hearing it all before. The promises, the plans, the hopes of a better life. Jimmy was four years younger and had probably not been listening, as she had, to the adult conversations that had flowed around them in the months before they left England.

There was no longer the same demand for a roof thatcher in the old country. And with so many mouths to feed, James Newell was forced to take on work that his wife thought was beneath him. When he fell in with poachers, to put food on the table, and only avoided arrest by luck and fast talking, Hannah persuaded him that they should try the colonies. She had heard that there was land for the taking – whole tracts of it being given away. Once they were landowners, she said, people would look up to them, as they did to the landed gentry in Sussex. They could even have servants. She quite fancied being waited on, instead of always having to wait on others.

After much discussion and argument over many months, the family finally set sail with high hopes of a better life in the Swan River Colony.

But by the time they arrived, all the best land had already been taken. Holdings with poor soil and no permanent water were all that was left. Besides, they were not farmers. James Newell had thought that, in a new colony, there would be a lot of building going on, houses needing roofs. They had thought that the wages he earned would sustain the family until they were well enough established on their own land. Hannah had been very excited about the prospect of being 'gentry'.

Now there was no land. And what grass there was in the wretched settlement was not suitable for thatching. There was just not enough of anything to go around. People, especially children, were dying of starvation and disease. At least in rural England there were doctors – if you could afford to pay. But there was no chance of going back. The family's meagre resources had all been used up in coming to Australia. The Newells were advised to cut their losses and try further south. There was another settlement, they were told, on the south coast, with plenty of land and a cooler climate.

But in King George Sound, the Newells found that things were even worse. When they had arrived, they had counted just seven houses perched above the natural harbour. All the livestock brought in to the colony had died and the few vegetables that managed to survive in the sandy soil could barely sustain the population. There was plenty of work to be done, but no one could afford to pay for it. By then, the Newells were desperate. There was nowhere else to go.

Then, in June 1833, Sir Richard Spencer arrived. He brought supplies, building materials, plants and livestock. Along with his wife, Lady Anne, and nine children, he brought eighteen servants. Matthew Gill had been one of them.

Two years went by and the tiny settlement at last began to prosper. Matthew saw other servants leaving their masters and taking up their own land. Although he had no resources and no real idea of what was involved, he decided to do the same. To add status to his new image of himself, he needed a wife.

The eligible young man arrived on the doorstep of James Newell, who was happy to offer either Dorothy or Mary. After all, he couldn't lose. Either he would be adding another able-bodied male, with earning potential, to his household, or the couple would live somewhere else, leaving him with one less mouth to feed.

Dorothy was the prettier of the two girls, but obviously bold and quick tempered. Matthew chose the shyer, gentler Mary.

On that stifling day in March 1835, Matthew Gill was the only one in the Newells' cottage above the harbour who showed any real interest in the news that Jimmy brought.

'It couldn't be worse than here,' Matthew said, conscious of his new responsibilities as a husband and perhaps, before too long, a father.

'Oh, Matthew.' Mary looked stricken. 'We couldn't leave the others.'

'They could come with us,' he said.

Around the room, the sudden intake of breath seemed to suck all the oxygen from the air, but the younger children, whose game had spilled out into the dirt beyond the doorway, shouted as they played, oblivious to the dramatic changes that would engulf them yet again.

After discussions long into the night, Matthew and Mary agreed to go with Jimmy. Dorothy went down to the dock with them while they negotiated a price. They found Captain Evanson Jansen, smelling strongly of alcohol, supervising the loading of stores into the *Mountaineer*'s whaleboat ready to be taken out to the anchored ship. The captain looked them up and down through narrowed bloodshot eyes, taking particular note of Dorothy's slim waist, full breasts and flowing auburn hair.

'Passage for four?' he asked.

'Three,' Dorothy said firmly, indicating the others.

'Is that so?' the man leaned towards her before catching hold of a post on the jetty to steady himself. 'Tell you what. Since I'm a sensitive man and don't like to see a family divided, I'll take all four for the price of three.' Dorothy was shaking her head, but the captain continued. 'Come on, you'll not get a better offer in this godforsaken place.'

'Sir Richard Spencer will turn things around, you'll see,' Matthew Gill said, leaping to the defence of his former master, whose farm at Strawberry Hill was already beginning to prosper.

'Ah, but in the meantime . . .' Captain Jansen said, nodding with great care before putting his free hand to his head.

Much as she disliked and distrusted this Captain Jansen, Dorothy's mind was working fast.

In the last few months, things had gone from bad to worse for the family. With so little paid work available, her father was spending more and more time adding to their debts by drinking at the pub.

'Don't fret, love, I'll make it good in no time,' James Newell would say to try and reassure his wife. 'Sir Richard will soon be needing more men to work his farm. And he'll not see us starve, I'll wager.'

Hannah, unable to cope with finding herself destitute in a totally alien land, forced to beg for food for her family, had begun drinking heavily. Dorothy even suspected that she was stealing alcohol, in desperation, from the small contingent of soldiers who were appointed to guard the fledgling settlement. Although when Dorothy challenged her, Hannah claimed the bottles of gin were gifts.

As the eldest in the family, Dorothy had always been expected to look after the younger children. She worried about leaving them, in particular her baby brother, William, barely two years old. But, reluctantly, she had to admit that the captain was right. It would take time for Sir Richard Spencer's reforms to make a difference to the settlement and by then – well, she wondered what state the family would be in. Two of her siblings had already died within a year of their birth. She couldn't bear to think of that happening to

William, who had become her favourite. Dorothy made a difficult decision.

Next morning, she joined her fourteen-year-old sister, Henrietta, who was doing the family's washing in the separate hut that contained the kitchen and laundry. Together, they carried the heavy basket, full of wet clothes, to the shrubs at the edge of the small clearing behind the house.

As they spread the washing out over the bushes to dry, Dorothy told her sister of the captain's offer. Henrietta was silent.

'You won't go, will you, Dolly?' she said at last, her face drained of colour.

'Only for a little while.' Dorothy tried to reassure her, but found it hard to keep the despair out of her own voice. 'I must do something. You can see that, can't you, Netty?'

'But what will *we* do without you?' Netty said, as the tears began.

'You're a big girl now.' Dorothy hugged her. 'Take care of the little ones. It won't be for long, and when I return there will be money for food and clothes and you will have the best present – whatever you wish for.'

This promise made no impact on Netty who had started to cry in earnest. But Dorothy's mind was made up.

'Come on, Mary.' Dorothy was already sitting in the ship's boat with Jimmy and Matthew. Two crewmen waited, gripping their oars, ready to take them out to the *Mountaineer*. Up on the wooden jetty, Mary still held their mother tightly.

The boat rocked as Jimmy, barely able to contain his impatience, stood and shouted up to them.

'The tide is on the turn and Captain Jansen can wait no longer!'

Mary planted one last kiss on the baby, hitched her skirts with one hand and made her way carefully down the narrow steps and into the boat. William squirmed in his mother's arms, trying to free himself to explore the jetty and the bright, moving water below.

Feeling that she had already lost her three older children, Hannah Newell tried desperately to keep a firm hold on the struggling William, and on herself.

She had taken to hiding the bottles. For the safety of the children, of course. An empty bottle could become a lethal weapon and, while James was normally the mildest of men, anything might happen after a long session at the pub. Or the children themselves might accidentally break one while playing their energetic games. She could not keep her eye on them every minute of the day. It was impossible to bring up children in these barbaric conditions with no hedged gardens and so many miles of untamed wilderness at her doorstep.

'We'll just have to make the most of it, I'm afraid,' James had told her.

When the Swan River Colony had turned out to be vastly different from what she had expected, there was still the hope that King George Sound would be better. Instead, it was worse. Much worse.

The small band of soldiers, stationed at the Sound to deter the French from claiming the land, were a rough and lawless bunch. So much so that when Sir Richard Spencer had first arrived he had asked for some of them to be removed and others sent in their place. Certainly, things were a little better now than before the Government Resident had come with his entourage. But it was all too late. Hannah Newell could not see how their hopes of becoming landowners could ever be realised.

Hannah watched the departing ship with a sinking heart. How would she manage the little ones without Dorothy's help? She had half expected to lose Mary. At the time, she had welcomed the marriage just as enthusiastically as James had. But suddenly Dorothy and Jimmy were gone too. Hannah Newell began to sink even further into depression and alcoholism.

17

NIGHT HAD FALLEN BY THE TIME THE *MOUNTAINEER* CLEARED THE heads at King George Sound. With a fair breeze filling her mainsail and the weather holding clear and mild, the prospect of a fast passage to Hobart began to dispel some of the anxieties of the crew. Most of them had joined the single-masted, 23-ton cutter in Fremantle and were working their passage to Sydney. They had been employed to replace more experienced sailors who had opted to stay and take their chances on shore in the Swan River Colony, rather than continue with the ship. For Evanson Jansen was not the most sober of captains.

After battling strong westerlies all the way down the coast, they were now running before them, heading east for Hobart and, after that, the bright lights of Sydney Cove.

In spite of the inexperience of his crew, Captain Jansen mostly stayed in his cabin, leaving them to manage the ship as best they could. When the captain did put in an appearance, it was usually to invite his passengers, especially the comely Dorothy Newell, to dine with him.

'Invited to dine with the captain!' Mary exclaimed. 'We really have come up in the world.'

Her sister was tempted to agree, but a frown creased her forehead. 'I just hope he keeps his hands to himself!'

At the captain's table that night, the four members of the Newell family group were not the only guests.

'Ah, ladies and gentlemen.' Captain Jansen ushered them in, indicating where each person should be seated and making sure that Dorothy was beside him. 'No doubt you have met Mr William Church.'

A thin man in a black whalebone-stiffened waistcoat laced tightly at the back rose to his feet as the women entered the room. He spoke softly and held out his hand, first to Matthew Gill, then to Jimmy Newell. 'I have been confined to my cabin by illness and by my work,' he explained, bowing his head to each of the ladies and resuming his seat only after they were settled in theirs.

'And what work is that, Mr Church?' Dorothy asked politely.

'I am making preparations to settle on a farm in Van Diemen's Land,' he said. 'It seems that the soil and climatic conditions there are much closer to those at home in England. That is, more conducive to the growing of familiar crops. I have much reading to do in order to acquaint myself fully with the situation.'

'You are a man of letters, then,' Matthew Gill commented. Jimmy Newell looked at Church with great respect, for he himself could neither read nor write. The older Newell children had sporadically attended the village school in Sussex. The two girls had learned to read a little and write their names, but Jimmy had never managed to unlock the mysteries of lines on paper.

'I was studying at the university in Oxford before our family suffered . . .' he cleared his throat, '. . . a series of misfortunes.'

'Oh?' Captain Jansen's curiosity – or perhaps an anxiety about his payment – had obviously been aroused. But if he had misgivings, he shrugged them off as he moved closer to Dorothy. 'Well then, here's to a pleasant voyage and a successful life in Van Diemen's Land,' he said, leaning over to touch his glass to hers. Around the table, the others joined him in the toast.

For seven days, the ship sailed sweetly before the wind under a blue and cloudless sky. The Newells spent their days lazing about on deck and their evenings dining, drinking and playing cards with the captain, if he was sober enough to concentrate on the game.

But as the days passed, it became increasingly clear that Evanson Jansen was more interested in the two women than he was in running his ship. For Mary, the unwanted attentions of Captain Jansen could be avoided by staying close to her husband. But Dorothy was in a much more difficult position. Her excuses of seasickness, fatigue or headache were largely ignored by Jansen, who, having given her a separate cabin, now felt he could come into it whenever he pleased. She used all her cunning, but it was difficult to keep avoiding the man in the close confines of a ship at sea. She thought of appealing to William Church, but he was a man of position, well above her lowly status. Besides, he was preoccupied with his books. Dorothy began to feel Captain Jansen's presence everywhere, hanging over her like the black clouds that had begun to gather thickly on the horizon.

During the early hours of 22 March the wind swung around to the north-west as a cyclone headed south. Throughout the morning, the sky darkened, and the swells continued to rise. First slapping at the hull, then breaking over the bow, white water flooded across the heaving deck and streamed away on either side.

The midshipman, Ernest Hill, went to wake the captain, but found him in such a drunken stupor that he could not be roused. The crew reefed the mainsail, then reefed again. But still the cutter heeled and slewed precariously.

With only the most rudimentary of charts at their disposal, and very little experience of the Southern Ocean, the men were undecided as to what they should do. From what they had seen of the coastline, it was rugged and inhospitable. But they wanted to keep it in view, fearing that the icebergs of Antarctica would pose just as big a threat, and having no clear idea of how far south they could safely go.

The wind howled and threw blinding rain into the face of the helmsman as he struggled to hold the ship's bow square to the mountainous seas. Already a veteran of ten years sailing between England and Van Diemen's Land, the *Mountaineer* creaked and groaned under the strain. It was only a matter of time before she was caught broadside on.

One giant wave caused her to keel over until she was in

danger of capsizing. There were shouts of panic from every quarter.

'Get another man on that helm!'

'Hold her fast!'

'She's goin' down!'

The gallant ship paused for a heart-stopping moment, then righted herself.

Captain Jansen was thrown out of his bunk onto the floor. He woke with a roar of rage and pain. By the time he had staggered up onto the deck, cliffs of black rock were looming on their port side.

'Hard a starboard, ye useless landlubbers!' the captain bellowed at the two men at the wheel. But the sea had the *Mountaineer* already in its grip and, while the crew scrambled to save her, she ran aground on the rocky promontory at Thistle Cove, about 240 miles east of Albany.

18

HUGE WAVES POUNDED THE *MOUNTAINEER*. HER DECKS WERE AWASH, her cabins flooded and her breached hull was splintering against the rocks.

'Lower the boat and lively about it!' Captain Jansen, suddenly shocked into sobriety, barked his order. Two crewmen struggled at the rail to get a boat over the side. The next wave reared up, spilled over them and swept them both into the sea. Their open mouths and thrashing arms disappeared below the churning water. They were never seen again.

The passengers clung to the mast or scrambled to the highest point of the steeply sloping deck while the rest of the crew worked to free the whaleboat from its lashings. The captain went below and came back with bulging pockets and a brandy cask slung across his shoulder.

'Watch how she goes there!' Jansen complained as the suspended boat crashed against the hull of the ship. But there was nothing the men could do. The roaring wind and heaving seas tossed the solid cedar whaleboat about as if it was made of matchsticks.

Ernest Hill flung a rope-ladder over the side and sent a

crewman, James Ward, down to try and steady the pitching boat. Then, clinging to each rung, the passengers descended. Meanwhile, Hill had managed to salvage a barrel of flour and had tied a quantity of sodden biscuits into his headscarf. These were lowered to the hands below.

Once everyone was on board the whaleboat, four of the men took the oars and the captain cast off the last remaining rope to set them free of the sinking ship. Some of her timbers had already broken away and swirled into the path of the whaleboat as if to delay its leaving, like a mother making one last appeal to her departing child.

In the bow of the boat, Mary and Dorothy sat huddled together, too cold and frightened to move. William Church, still in his frock coat with his black felt hat jammed firmly over his ears, was hunched between James Ward and Ernest Hill. With Jimmy and Matthew on the other pair of oars and Captain Jansen in the stern they rowed in silence, inching the boat away from the shattered ship that had so recently held their hopes for the future.

'What will become of us, Dolly?' Mary cried as the pitching motion of the boat threw them against each other.

Dorothy didn't reply. She continued to stare straight ahead, mouth clamped shut, arms wrapped tightly across her breasts. She was determined not to let her body betray the fear she felt.

The whaleboat with its eight occupants struggled around the promontory into relative calm. The bay at Thistle Cove was small, with a narrow strip of beach and low scrub covering the sandhills. Once the boat was beached, they looked for shelter. After finding only a shallow cave in a corner of the bay, they rigged up the single sail from the whaleboat to provide some protection. At last, as darkness gathered, they lay down to rest.

In the morning, the survivors woke to clear blue skies. The storm had passed and the sun beat down on clean white sand and sparkling sea. They looked at each other's red-rimmed eyes and ran parched tongues around their dry mouths. Fine sand, blown by the relentless wind, had collected in their hair and clung to every moist corner of their faces, giving them the look of badly made up clowns.

James Ward and Ernest Hill set off up the sandhill to search for water. Dorothy, who had fallen fully clothed into an exhausted sleep the previous evening, stripped off her shoes and stockings, hitched up her skirts and waded into the ocean. Mary quickly followed. The two young women scooped up the dancing water and splashed it onto their faces, clearing their eyes and cooling their cheeks. Then they took off their bonnets and shook out their hair. At one point, they stood back and laughed at each other as if they were on a seaside outing.

But when, after several hours, the two men came back without fresh water, an air of gloom descended once again on the group.

On the second day, they saw a thin column of smoke rising into the sky about a mile inland.

'Blackfellers,' Jansen declared. 'They'll know where to find water.'

But when Ward and Hill hurried towards the smoke, it disappeared. Again they came back to the beach empty handed. While Captain Jansen surreptitiously sipped his brandy, the others prised tiny limpets off the rocks and sucked at their juicy flesh. But the relief they gave was short lived. The salt they contained only increased everyone's thirst.

By the third day, curiosity had enticed the Aborigines closer. When three men, spears at the ready, finally appeared silhouetted against the sky, Captain Jansen tried to communicate with them. The Aborigines watched, stock still and staring. Ward and Hill approached cautiously, carrying their canvas buckets. After much pointing and sign language, the men were taken to a pool of water hidden among some rocks that shielded it from the sun. The water was stagnant and brackish, but drinkable.

Each day, different members of the shipwrecked party wandered aimlessly up and down the beach, scanning the horizon for any sign of a passing ship. But none came.

To relieve their boredom, some of the castaways hunted the tiny crabs and scuttling shellfish that lived in the rock pools. The ones they managed to catch supplemented the salty damper they made each evening by mixing flour with sea water and cooking it in the coals of their fire.

William Church, however, amused himself in a different way. He sat without speaking, barely moving, in the shade of the sail for the first two days. In spite of the heat, he still wore his tightly laced waistcoat over his shirt. He carried a leather satchel on a long strap that hung from one shoulder and crossed his chest, keeping the satchel high up under his left arm, where it was protected from the weather and, no doubt, from light fingers and prying eyes. He clutched it to him even when he slept, as if it contained something so precious that he would die before he would allow anyone to touch it.

Eventually, thirst forced him to make the journey to the pool with the others. On the way back, Dorothy tried to engage him in conversation.

'Why did ya leave England, Mr Church?'

'Opportunities, Miss Newell, and escape.' He paused to study Dorothy's face, as if deciding how much to tell, but continued when she nodded encouragingly. 'I had thought to make a new start. But I was misled, cheated by some unscrupulous devils at Swan River Colony.'

'So were we,' Dorothy said. She was amazed that, although Church was 'landed gentry', a class always envied by her parents, his story was so similar to her own.

'The land they sold me was useless. Everything died. I tried to run sheep, but their digestive systems were not accustomed to the native grasses, the hard saltbush.'

Without any sign to Dorothy, he stopped walking and peered at one of the bushes they had just passed. Dorothy left him to join the others.

The sailors claimed the reddish-brown berries on these bushes were poisonous, but William Church never intended to eat them. When he had gathered enough, he crushed the juice from them, produced a small bottle from his satchel and carefully strained the liquid into it through his linen handkerchief. Then he took out a quill pen and a bound notebook.

Back under the shade of the sail, intermittently dipping his pen in the 'ink', he would write, sometimes for hours on end, filling up pages with tiny squiggly words. Since no one else in the group was particularly skilled at reading and writing, this seemed to them like a lot of wasted effort.

19

'THERE'S BOUND TO BE A SHIP,' CAPTAIN JANSEN INSISTED. 'ANY day now.'

He dismissed their fears with an impatient wave of his hand when anyone mentioned that their supply of flour was being quickly depleted and that none of them had succeeded in killing any of the native animals or birds. The level of water in the rocky pool was also dropping noticeably.

As the days went by with no sails breaking the horizon, the stranded group became increasingly desperate. Dorothy worried about Mary, who had been lying listlessly under the shelter for two days and was now refusing to eat. Both Dorothy and Matthew had tried to persuade her, but she complained of fatigue and would no longer even walk the few metres across the beach to cool her feet in the sea.

'We're all going to die here, aren't we?' Mary said, her voice coming from low in her throat.

'No, my darling. You must not say that. You must not even think it!'

But it was what most of them were thinking. Even Captain Jansen no longer strutted up and down the beach, prattling about women in exotic ports, or the delights of Hobart Town.

By the tenth day the flour was gone. The group's attempts at hunting game had still been unsuccessful. They had caught a few fish in the traps that Hill and Ward had woven from native grasses but, on its own, this source of nourishment would not sustain a party of eight people for long. Captain Jansen finally conceded that something would have to be done. They must put to sea again, he declared, while they still had strength to row.

'What, back to King George Sound?' Jimmy asked.

'There's nowhere closer,' Ernest Hill pointed out.

'Ah, not so,' Jansen said. His eyes, always slightly out of line, rolled in his head, emphasising the look of madness that had begun to settle on his face. 'Not so,' he said again. Wagging one finger for emphasis, he pulled a small whiskey flask from his pocket. Tilting his head back, he drained the last drop. While reluctantly sharing his barrel of brandy, he had kept this extra supply of liquor hidden until now. In spite of their doubts about him, everyone gathered around to hear what the captain had to say.

'On my last voyage to Hobart Town, I took advantage of the hospitality of Captain Merredith on Kangaroo Island. He is of the opinion that there are . . . sealers . . . on Middle Island.'

'Where is that?' asked William Church.

'I've not been there in person,' Jansen confessed. 'But I believe it is one, perhaps two days from here.' Ernest Hill and James Ward exchanged glances that did not go unnoticed by Jansen. ''Tis true, Anderson will not be well pleased, but what choice do we have?'

'Black Jack Anderson, the pirate?' Like everyone else in King George Sound, Jimmy Newell had heard the stories.

'Aye, the most feared and hated man in the whole of the Southern Ocean,' Ernest Hill confirmed.

'And the best seaman,' James Ward added.

'Hunph! That's a matter of opinion!' The slightly built Jansen gave a dismissive wave of his hand. 'The man's a villain and a rogue. I myself would not trust him even so far as I could throw him!'

'Which would not be far,' muttered Ward.

'Aye,' Ernest Hill agreed. 'A giant of a man and no mistake!'

'So?' Jansen replied scornfully. ''Twill mean he falls the harder. A British captain with his wits about him need never fear that damned Yankee!' Evanson Jansen drew himself up to his full height, which was not much over five feet. The thought of a confrontation between the two made the other men laugh out loud. Jansen glared at them.

'How long will it take to reach this island?' William Church enquired.

'If we can find it,' Ernest Hill added.

Jansen furrowed his brow in a thoughtful way, but only succeeded in looking more shifty. 'By ship, a day or two,' he said.

'And by whaleboat?' Church asked.

The captain's eyes began to wander again, forcing him to blink rapidly. 'Depends who's doin' the rowin',' he said, peering with some difficulty at Church.

The group set about preparing to leave Thistle Cove.

They dismantled their shelter and fitted the mast and

sail back into the whaleboat. The fish traps that the sailors had woven were placed on board along with the flour barrel, which they had managed to half fill with water. William Church gathered more berries, wrapping them carefully in his white linen handkerchief now stained with salt and juice. Jimmy and Matthew set about putting out the embers from their fire and burying the coals.

At last, the whaleboat put to sea once more.

The breeze was fair so they hoisted the sail. Captain Jansen took the steering oar and turned their bow towards the southeast. Mary looked back to the beach that had been their home for ten days. The sun shone relentlessly on its fringe of grey-green bush. Foam-edged water lapped the white sand, forming the same timeless patterns as it had before they arrived and would go on doing long after they were gone. It was a desolate place. She had hated and feared it. But now her greater fear of what lay ahead made it seem familiar, even comforting.

Dorothy, on the other hand, stared straight out to sea, refusing to turn her head.

20

THE DAY STRETCHED ENDLESSLY FOR THE OCCUPANTS OF THE OVER-
crowded whaleboat. Cramped by the fish traps and water
barrel, constantly drenched with salt spray, their skin, already
burnt by the sun, pulled tight and finally cracked in the relentless wind. But they needed the wind. When it dropped, the
men had to bend their protesting bodies to the oars. Even
the sailors among them were beginning to show signs of
exhaustion.

With her stomach emptied by seasickness, Dorothy sat
gripping the gunwale with one hand, her eyes closed against
the glare of the ocean. A flock of gulls circled overhead. Their
harsh cries forced her to look up at them. Reluctantly, she
tracked their dark shapes as they passed across the empty
blue sky.

When they were gone, she lapsed once more into a trance-
like state.

There was movement in the boat. Dorothy opened her eyes.
She was surprised to see that the horizon was no longer empty.
A small island lay behind them and they were already in the

lee of another, slightly larger, one. On its northern and eastern shores, sheltered from the pounding sea, tough straggly bushes and succulent pigface plants could be seen growing in the sandy soil. On the south side, dozens of sleek, brown seals lay on a bare, rocky slope.

'Belay, lads,' Captain Jansen shouted. 'We'll rest here and feast on seal tonight.'

But by the time the weary men had found a sheltered cove and beached the boat, the seals were sliding, swiftly and gracefully, into the sea. The fish traps had to be brought into service once more and, although the captain was none too pleased about missing out on seal meat for his dinner, everyone made themselves as comfortable as possible and settled down to wait until morning.

The next day was again spent painfully exposed to sun, wind and waves. About an hour before dark, they landed on an island. To the *Mountaineer*'s passengers, every island looked the same. They felt that they were travelling in circles on an endless voyage without hope of ever finding another human soul. But the relief of being on dry land, even temporarily, was enormous.

Dorothy stepped out of the boat on legs that would barely support her. Mary, still staring at the horizon, seemed unable to move. Between them, Dorothy and Matthew helped her onto the sand, where she collapsed. As Dorothy rubbed her sister's legs to get some circulation going, she noticed how dry and cracked her own hands had become.

While the other men scattered to look for water and

anything that might be edible, William Church gathered wood and lit a fire using his tinderbox, carefully kept dry inside that amazing waistcoat of his. Dorothy watched him and wondered about his age. Under his wide-brimmed black hat the shoulder-length hair was dark, without the traces of grey that were obvious in Evanson Jansen's oiled pigtail. He spoke very little, but when he did, his voice was soft, educated. Most of the time, he sat, hunched over with concentration, trying to write in his notebook. His craggy face with the prominent cheekbones reminded Dorothy of a picture of Moses that she had seen in her grandmother's Bible. William Church had remained calm, almost detached, throughout the drama of the shipwreck and the ordeal on the beach. Here he was, gathering wood, lighting a fire. The orange-and-blue flames that he coaxed into life provided the only splash of colour on the bleak, windswept island. Dorothy encouraged Mary to come in closer to the fire. Their clothes dried stiffly, chafing against their damaged skin. But they fell asleep in spite of the discomfort.

For three days they continued in this way, sailing or rowing on the blazing sea during the long hours of daylight, resting each night, as best they could, on one of the many small islands. Caught in a limbo of hunger, thirst and wet clothes, they sank into deep despair. No one spoke. When the wind dropped, they sat, rocking on the waves, until Jansen roused himself enough to prod his oarsmen. Bending to their task, each man revealed vertebrae protruding like a ridge of rocks under his clinging shirt.

When most of the party had resigned themselves to existing forever in this suspended state, a shout went up from Captain Jansen.

'Ahoy! Look alive now, ye scurvy, landlubbin' lot!' he croaked. His hand on the steering oar had cramped like a claw, but he immediately turned the boat, head on, into the easterly wind. 'Didn't I tell ya? Old Davey Jones will not be seein' us for a while yet.' He was obviously pleased with himself, but when the others looked at the speck of land they were approaching, it seemed just as barren and desolate as every other landfall they had made. Captain Jansen pointed out Cape Arid and assured them that their destination was not far off.

For two more hours they laboured into the wind, tacking where they could, the men dipping their oars with what little strength they had left.

The island, when they drew closer, looked exactly like all the others they had seen. The occupants of the whaleboat stared through half-closed, bloodshot eyes. There was a matching hopelessness to their sagging bodies. *Another disappointment.* It was written on their faces, along with the other unspoken question: *How much longer before a merciful death comes?*

During that third day, Mary had slumped in the bottom of the boat. Since none of the others had the strength to raise her, she lay there, flopped about by the motion of the sea.

Suddenly, as if hell had finally opened its gates with a fanfare of trumpets to receive them, a cacophony of honking sounds erupted. A whole flock of Cape Barren Geese took to the air above the boat.

'I knew it!' Jansen cried, lifting his sagging shoulders and extending one arm. Men who could barely hold up their heads raised themselves to look. 'Middle Island!'

Urging them to one last effort, the captain steered the whaleboat through the narrow entrance to a horseshoe-shaped bay.

21

ANDERSON WAS THE UNDISPUTED LEADER OF MIDDLE ISLAND AND nothing in this regard had changed over the course of seven years. He was bigger, stronger and could think faster than any of the men and he knew how to inspire loyalty. Paine and Winterbourne had proven their worth; Gimble had Anderson's full trust. Manning, however, was still on the outer.

After first arriving on the island, it hadn't taken Manning long to decide that he would be best off sharing in the wealth accumulated from raiding ships before leaving to start a new life, but Anderson had never allowed him to go on one of these outings. After a time, Manning made some unsuccessful attempts to get off the island, but he had to be careful. Those who threw in their lot with the pirates knew that it was unwise to cross Anderson. The body of one of his enemies, throat cut from ear to ear, was on display behind a waterfall on Doubtful Island, near King George Sound. The constantly flowing water preserved it, and for years it sat there as a warning.

No one could say exactly how or when the body was placed there, but Anderson never denied responsibility. Then again, he never admitted it either.

Standing on the ridge above the beach, his arms folded across his massive chest, Anderson watched as the whaleboat approached. Its keel bumped and dragged on the seabed, throwing the occupants against each other. Two men eventually struggled out on cramped legs, splashing about as they tried to bring it to shore.

Anderson neither moved nor spoke. Visitors were not welcome on Middle Island.

With the boat now broadside on to the waves, others began to tumble out. Anderson spat his contempt. It had been six years since his raid on the *Mountaineer*, but even so he recognised the incompetent Jansen. Two women, ridiculous in bonnets and full skirts, lay on the sand where they had fallen.

When all the survivors had made it to shore, Anderson came down from the ridge. Jansen saw him and raised himself on hands and knees. Anderson examined the boat, found it to be sound, and pulled it up above the waterline with deft movements of his arms and shoulders.

'I managed to save some brandy.' The wheedling voice of the captain rose on the wind. Anderson ignored him.

'Water . . .' It was Dorothy who spoke. Anderson paused, regarding her with almost neutral curiosity.

'Up that way,' he said, and disappeared into the scrub that walled the narrow beach.

James Manning was always alert to anything unusual. He approached the survivors, who were now barely moving.

'Will he kill us?' Jimmy Newell asked.

'He's none too pleased,' Manning said.

'For pity's sake, we must have water,' Dorothy pleaded.

'He'll not deny you that.' Manning laughed, examining the woman before him. In spite of her bedraggled state, her stained hems, the raw and bleeding patch of skin where the salt-stiff ribbon of her bonnet had chafed her neck, there was something attractive about her. But her gaunt, emaciated body did not stir his rather fastidious passion.

Manning led the group over the limestone ridge to the clearing under the stand of paperbark trees. Dorothy helped Mary to her feet, but the two women struggled to keep up. Several times they stopped to rest. When they reached the clearing, they found Jimmy, Matthew and the other men from the *Mountaineer* already blending in among the tough-looking group of sealers. Most of them were lounging around an open fire. Two water buckets rolled on their sides. They were both empty, but the men's shirts were still wet at their necks from drinking too hastily.

Hesitating on the edge of this gathering, Dorothy looked them over. Some stared as if they had never seen a woman before. Others seemed to be pretending, or perhaps wishing, she and Mary were not there. Anderson was in discussion with a man whose coarse brown hair stood up from his forehead and whose bushy sideburns joined a long and equally bushy beard, giving him the appearance of a big man when, without the hair, he could have walked under Anderson's outstretched arm. Narrow eyes flicked towards Dorothy, then back to Anderson. Dorothy had the uncomfortable feeling that they were discussing her and she turned away.

James Manning stood with Jimmy on the edge of the

group. Manning looked younger than the rest and seemed out of place. Dorothy thought he looked the least threatening.

'Please . . .'

'If you take that path, you'll find the well,' Manning said dismissively. He indicated a worn track that led around behind the bush-timber and stone hut. Then, possibly relenting a little, he picked up one of the wooden ship's buckets with a length of rope tied to the handle and handed it to Jimmy.

William Church attempted to rise from the flat rock he was sitting on, but his legs gave way and he slumped back awkwardly. Matthew Gill lay stretched out on his back, eyes closed, but Dorothy picked up the second bucket and set off with Jimmy and Mary.

The path was narrow. Dorothy and Mary struggled behind Jimmy, trying to keep up. Behind the hut, the ground sloped up towards the beach. They followed the lower path along the sheltered gully and came to a bare expanse of weathered rock. Centuries of run-off had left broad watermarks of orange, grey and black striping the granite outcrop. Patches of blackened moss lay like discarded pincushions, waiting for the rains to come and turn them soft and green again.

Mary stopped, panting from her exertions.

'How much further?' she pleaded as she collapsed to the ground. Dorothy and Jimmy looked at each other. The wind soughed through the trees. An occasional shout of laughter or protest reached them from the clearing, but the bush that surrounded them seemed utterly deserted.

'Wait there,' Dorothy said, lifting her sister's drooping face until their eyes met. 'Jimmy and I will go.'

'Don't leave me!' Mary cried.

Dorothy hesitated for a moment, then she grabbed Jimmy's bucket, pushed past him and followed the bend in the track.

In the next hollow, Dorothy saw a raised circle of rough stones topped by a raft of stripped branches laced together to form a lid. Her steps quickened as she moved towards it. In her weakened state, she struggled to lift the cover. But she knew there was water below. Gathering all her strength, she heaved it so that it slid away from her and came to rest at an angle, like one half of a pitched roof.

Jimmy arrived half carrying, half dragging Mary.

The three drank and washed and drank again until their bellies swelled. Their limbs relaxed and they lay down, resting their backs and shoulders. Out of the wind, the sun was warm and the women fell asleep.

Jimmy rested with his back against a rock. Then, not wanting to wake his sisters, he filled the buckets and made his way back to the clearing.

Dorothy woke to the sight of a prehistoric-looking creature dangling inches from her face.

She screamed. Mary sat up beside her and they both scrambled backwards over the rock.

A cackle of laughter came from the hideous, gaping mouth of a man who stood swinging the large, dead lizard by its tail, waving it in their faces.

'Get that thing away!' Dorothy screeched. Mary hid her face in her skirt.

Then Anderson appeared.

'He don't mean nothin' by it. Do you, Johnno?' He laughed loudly as the other man held the lizard by its front legs and made it perform some lifelike bowing gestures.

Dorothy stood up and straightened her skirt. Anderson's eyes did not waver and yet he seemed to take in everything at once. He reached out and placed one hand on Dorothy's arm. Dorothy shrank from his touch.

Anderson's outstretched hand snatched the lizard from Johnno. 'Cook's a-waitin' for this,' he said, and strode away, with Johnno trailing after him.

22

THE SISTERS STAYED, RESTING WHERE THEY WERE FOR A TIME, UNTIL eventually Dorothy became aware of another presence. The continuous voice of the sea, the scuttling movements of banded lizards, the harsh cries of crows and gulls became suddenly muted. She stood up slowly.

'What is it?' Mary pushed herself into a sitting position.

Two black women were standing perfectly still, camouflaged among the shadows of the tree trunks. Only the strings of shells they wore around their necks, pale against their brown skin, made them visible.

All four women stood regarding each other. Then Dorothy stepped forward.

'Hello,' she said. When there was no answer, she added, 'I'm Dorothy Newell. This is my sister Mary.'

Both of the black women lowered their eyes, but they did not back away. Dorothy took another step towards them, her hand outstretched. The taller of the two spoke softly, raising one slender arm and pointing back towards the hut. 'Boss say you sleep longa fire. There.'

'Thank you,' Dorothy said, making no attempt to move, in

spite of the implied instruction. There was another long pause in which no one spoke. Finally, the Aboriginal women turned and disappeared into the bush without a twig breaking or a leaf rustling.

The men in the clearing were swapping stories. Bursts of ribald laughter died away as Dorothy and Mary appeared. Nurla and Biddi were already inside the hut preparing food. Quickly and skilfully, they prepared the lizard for meat, peeled sweet potatoes and placed them all together in the large pot suspended by a ship's chain and pulley above the coals in the fireplace.

While Nurla squatted before the fire, stoking it with fresh logs, Biddi stirred and browned the meat and potatoes in seal oil, moving them around the pot so that they wouldn't burn. The flames licked higher. Biddi added a little water from the wooden pail on the floor. Steam hissed and poured into the room, bringing with it a delicious smell of roasting.

Dorothy ate some of the delicious damper, but her shrunken stomach could not accommodate the meat, even though it now bore no resemblance to the creature that had terrified and disgusted her. Mary could barely keep her eyes open, so the two women retired gratefully.

With their mugs full of rum, the men had gathered around one end of the table. Jimmy and Matthew shared a pannikin. Such a sudden influx of drinkers meant there were not enough of the roughly moulded mugs to go around. Until white clay from the salt lake could be shaped and fired in the 'kiln' where the seal blubber was rendered, drinking vessels had to be improvised for the newcomers.

An oily pack of playing cards appeared and wooden chips were distributed. The game seemed to have different rules from those known to the *Mountaineer*'s survivors, who were soon in trouble for cheating. A struggle broke out between Jansen and Winterbourne. Punches were thrown and Winterbourne's arm quickly circled Jansen's neck. Jansen was reaching for his knife when Anderson's powerful fist came down on the table with a shuddering thump.

'Belay there!' His voice boomed in the crowded room. As Gimble and Ernest Hill dragged the combatants apart, Anderson's arm swept cards and chips onto the dirt floor. The game was over.

Winterbourne showed the newcomers to the pile of bedrolls, making sure that they took only the most worn ones, and indicated where they could spread them. Matthew Gill joined Mary and Dorothy.

'Useless scum,' Winterbourne grumbled, returning to the table once the job was done.

'Their boat be sound,' Anderson said. 'And three of them be seamen. Preacher-man, he ain't no use for that, but he can still work plenty. Ain't no one gonna be idle on this island.'

'And the redheaded woman ain't doin' my eyes any harm, either,' Mead added to peels of laughter.

'Deal, Gimble. A fresh start!' Anderson declared, changing the subject.

The season had been good so far. The value of the pile of skins in the storeroom was mounting, which meant that the stakes at these nightly card games were high.

The men concentrated on the cards once more, talking in low voices as they leaned inwards, their heads almost touching. The lamp on the table burned low, throwing a softening light on the circle of intense faces. It smoothed out their scarred features and flashed on their remaining teeth. Laughter and comradely banter was heard more often as the effects of the rum took hold.

The chips of wood used as tokens began to pile up in front of Anderson, and Manning seethed silently but only Winterbourne continued to curse and call into question any interpretation of the rules that he didn't agree with.

23

IT WAS BARELY LIGHT WHEN MARY AWOKE. MATTHEW WAS NO longer by her side.

She got up and stepped into the semi-darkness, leaving Dorothy sound asleep.

Strong winds had been blowing across the island, bending the tops of the taller trees and flapping the strips of paperbark that hung forlornly from the pale trunks. But the early morning air was surprisingly calm. A sharp salt-marsh smell drifted from the lake as the sealers moved away from the clearing, making their way down to the beach. Mary saw that the men from the *Mountaineer* were with them. She struggled to the top of the ridge above the beach, anxious about what plans had been made for her husband and her brother, but unable to intervene.

From the sloping rock at one end of the beach, Anderson gave instructions. The whaleboat from the *Mountaineer* had been launched beside Anderson's own, and Nurla and Biddi were sitting, one in the bow of each boat, looking out to sea.

Anderson was allocating men to each of the oars when an argument broke out between Winterbourne and Ward.

Winterbourne's voice grew louder and he grabbed Ward by the throat.

William Church, who had been standing with Ward, tried to separate the two men.

'Wait,' he said, holding up his open hands as if about to deliver a blessing. But Winterbourne, whose fist was already drawn back, swung at Church instead and hit him full in the face. Church fell backwards. Stunned, he looked up at Winterbourne who stood above him, about to deliver a kick to the fallen man's ribs. In two strides Anderson was there. He grabbed Winterbourne by the hair, dragging him upright and shoving him towards the boat before reaching down and offering his hand to Church. 'You ain't comin' sealin' with us. But make yo'self useful here or you be makin' yo'self useful in the next life.'

Gimble and Mead shoved one boat out, guiding it through the low swells into deeper water before taking their places at the oars. Hill and Ward did the same with the other. The oarsmen's bodies swung forward and back, their well-oiled rowlocks clicking in unison, oars slicing and pulling with barely a splash as the two boats crossed the bay and headed out to sea.

Mary watched until they disappeared behind Goose Island, then returned to Dorothy.

Later, while Mary rested, Dorothy walked along the beach, crossed the rocky point and found herself in a smaller cove. A pair of dolphins played in the rising swells. Their glistening bodies looped in and out of the water, sometimes in unison, sometimes weaving and turning away. The permanent smiles on their faces reminded her of children teasing each other. As she approached the next rocky point, waves rolling in from the west crashed against the granite cliff, sending their spray high into the air to drift and fall on her like gentle rain. Deceptively gentle, for she knew only too well the power of those waves.

When there was no more soft white sand to walk on, she left the beach and climbed up through the scrub, picking her way between the bushes. Some of them reached up and spread out above her head, others grew low to the ground, and caught at her long, cumbersome skirts. But she kept climbing until she emerged on the bare granite cap of the highest peak. The wind was much stronger on the exposed rock. She was surprised by how much effort it took to stand firm. The sea lay far below, stretching to the horizon in all directions except one. She turned towards the north where the dark hump of the mainland rose out of the water.

From where she stood, the immense continent appeared to be just another island, but larger than the others, which were not much more than tiny brown dots surrounded by a ragged frill of surf. The granite dome of Cape Arid jutted out of the haze while the rest of the coastline curved back and away, disappearing from sight. It was strange to think of people, somewhere in the mists on either side of that bare black cliff, greeting their neighbours, tending their houses, working in their gardens.

Dorothy thought of the makeshift shelter on the beach at Thistle Cove and decided they must organise something similar. She and Mary would need more protection from the men than Matthew alone could offer, and the canvas might not do much good but at least it would provide a shelter from prying eyes, as well as from the sun and rain.

She made her way back to the clearing. Although she was wary of the sealers, without them the island felt more desolate and depressing than ever. The harsh cries of gulls overhead and the rustlings of wild, scaly creatures below sent shivers through her.

24

FROM THE SHELTER THAT JIMMY AND MATTHEW HAD ERECTED, Dorothy could hear voices and the sounds of men moving around, though it was not yet light.

Mary was sleeping beside her, breathing raggedly. In the couple of weeks they had been on Middle Island, Dorothy had made a full recovery from their ordeal. Mary, however, was increasingly unable to rouse herself.

Once the boats went out, Dorothy walked. She had done the same thing at King George Sound. In those seemingly far-off days, it had been a luxury to be alone. Walking had given her a short respite from the constant demands of her family. Now it helped to clear her mind and give her a sense of purpose. She couldn't decide which she dreaded most, the emptiness when the boats were away at sea or the unwanted attentions of the sealers, who seemed to make a point of brushing against her or leaning across her on the slightest pretext.

Anderson kept his distance, regarding them all with the slightly aloof air of a general inspecting his troops. But he was aware of her.

Dorothy firmly believed that a ship would come, from

either direction, she didn't care which, and they would be picked up and taken to a safer place. Although, leaving the island would be dangerous. The huge pirate had made it clear that he did not want the location of his camp to become common knowledge. The unwritten law of the sea had obliged him to offer safety to those whose lives were in danger. But it did not require him to be happy about it.

Then Dorothy began to notice Anderson's presence at crucial times.

William Church would later write:

There was ice between them. A brittle coldness, melted slowly over time by the heat of their bodies. The small, almost accidental collisions became more frequent and chipped away at the sharp corners until large cracks appeared. It was the beginning of the thaw.

After dinner one evening, Jansen and Hill had been leaning their heads together, glancing at Dorothy and sniggering.

'Dolly,' Jansen called, beckoning with a gnarled finger. Anger and disgust fought for supremacy in her chest.

'Dorothy!' she corrected him.

'Come, my dear,' Jansen said, still smiling knowingly at Hill. 'Your brother calls you Dolly and so will I, since we are practically married.'

Anderson stood up slowly from his place at the table. Jansen glanced towards him and was met by a steely stare from those eyes that always appeared to be looking into the distance, but never missed the vital details close at hand.

Dorothy glared angrily at them both. Then she spun on

her heel and fled back to the shelter. Anderson lifted his head to survey the room. He paused long enough to ensure that Dorothy would not be followed, then he returned his attention to the game.

For such a big man, Anderson moved very quietly. One minute he was not there, the next minute he was, suddenly appearing in the doorway of the hut, or holding back the seal-skin curtain that divided his private room from the kitchen. His arrival always brought a semblance of order to the rowdy group of seamen.

Increasingly, Dorothy had reasons to be grateful for his interventions. But would he let her go when the time came? Now that they knew the whereabouts of his camp, would he let any of them go? Perhaps he would bargain with her, as he had with Jansen.

A new wave of anger and resentment against the drunken captain rose in Dorothy's throat. But then she remembered how close to death they had all come. It was no use blaming anyone. They were alive. They had food, water and shelter. They would manage, somehow.

At the end of one day, Anderson came up from the beach in a foul mood. Jimmy was trailing behind Manning. He was obviously exhausted. His gait was unusual – slow and limping. His trouser legs were torn and his feet were cut and bleeding. Anderson had lost patience with these weaker men but when he saw Dorothy running to her brother, he left to seek out the calming presence of Nurla and Biddi.

Jimmy shrugged off the hand Dorothy placed on his arm. ''Tis nothin', Dolly.'

'Thought he was one of the blackfellas for a minute there, didn't we, mate?' Manning laughed in a humourless way.

They had reached the clearing amid more laughter from the men.

'Yeah, swimmin' with the seals,' Jansen said.

'But he can't swim!' Dorothy was horrified.

'He can now,' they told her. Jimmy, obviously embarrassed, shook his head at her. Dorothy looked around at the squinting eyes, the scarred faces, the gaps between blackened teeth in their open mouths. She hated them all.

It was clear to the others that if Jimmy hadn't proved so useful, relieving Manning of the menial but often dangerous tasks forced on him by Anderson and his men, Manning would not have given him the time of day. But Jimmy seemed not to notice. At mealtime that night, the slightly inebriated Jimmy dropped his knife. Manning kicked it under the table, covered it with his foot and watched with a smirk on his face while Jimmy searched long and hard for it.

Later, primed with tuna baked in the coals and a generous serve of rum, Gimble told the story of how the fishing net had snagged between some rocks. It was Manning's job, since he was the youngest, lightest and most able to fit himself into small spaces, to scramble down the wet and slippery rocks and free the gear. But he hated this sort of task and saw an opportunity to send Jimmy in his place.

'Right you are,' Jimmy had called, wanting to please

Manning and show himself equal to any man. Slipping and sliding on the wet rocks in his haste and eagerness, he had reached out his hand towards the snagged net. At that moment, a huge wave had broken over the rocks and sucked Jimmy into the sea.

Amid shouts and laughter, the others had tried to help while he thrashed his arms and gasped for air. In the end, it was the snagged net that had saved him. He had grabbed it and hung there, like a stranded starfish, while three more huge waves tried to shake him free. After the set had passed, Jimmy had struggled back up to where the waiting hands of the men had helped him to safety.

'What about the net, lad?' With broad grins on their faces, they had chided him and slapped him on the back as he coughed up sea water. Anderson had stopped the chaos with a roar and ordered Manning to go down and retrieve the net himself.

In the hut, Manning sat sullenly apart while the rest of the group recalled the events of the day and added other stories.

When the group began to break up, Gimble brought his rum and sat between William Church and Jimmy.

'I'd not be gettin' too close to your man over there,' Gimble said, nudging Jimmy and nodding towards Manning.

'Why not?' Jimmy asked.

'He is not a seaman,' William Church observed quietly.

'No, more's the pity, since the Fates seem hell bent on throwin' him in,' Gimble laughed.

But Jimmy was a simple soul, and would always fall prey to more worldly characters.

Mary, on the other hand, was not taken in by anyone and longed to get away from them all. She missed her mother and Netty. How would they manage? At least there were three less mouths to feed. Suddenly, the thought of them being better off without her brought a lump to her throat.

She had noticed the wind and cloud patterns changing. Winter was coming. There would be no ships during the cold, dark months when storms raged up from Antarctica, whipping the sea into a black fury. Even at the Sound, life became more difficult in winter. In spite of the sheltering hollow on Middle Island, Mary could not imagine how they would survive under their flimsy awning. But so far, she had not been able to think of an escape plan that would not expose them to even greater danger.

25

BY THE END OF THREE WEEKS, THE NEW ARRIVALS HAD SETTLED INTO their routines. Towards nightfall, the sealing party returned. The boats were beached in the bay and seal carcasses carried inland to the salt lake where Nurla and Biddi began boiling down the blubber in a whaler's trypot. Dorothy wondered, as she had about other items, where the heavy iron pot had come from and how the pirates had managed to transport it across the sea to Middle Island. Soon the pervasive smell of blood and bone began to waft over the hut.

Dorothy and Mary brought their harvest of vegetables and the two Aboriginal women brought meat to the kitchen. They emptied the pot of what little water was left in it and greased it thoroughly, diced the dark red meat and threw the pieces into the pot, where they stirred and turned them until they were seared on the outside. Dorothy and Mary cleaned and peeled vegetables, which Biddi chopped while Nurla heaped flour onto the table and made a hollow in the centre of the pile. Slowly adding water, she kneaded and folded the mixture, rolled it into balls and set them aside. Later, they would be placed in the pot, where they turned into dumplings that soaked up the juices of the meat and vegetables.

When the food was ready, Biddi carried the pot lid and a roughly fashioned wooden spoon to the doorway. Beating the two together, she created a sound which resonated through the clearing and beyond.

'Grub ho!' shouted Church. His skin had tanned and his daily tasks had put muscles on his slight frame. His bony elbows looked like chicken's knees.

The men gathered. With battered pewter plates in their gnarled hands, they crowded around the pot, jostling each other as they helped themselves to the thick stew. Anderson ate first. With a piece of damper held in his hand, he scooped up the food and shoved it into his mouth, always keeping a watchful eye on the others.

Space was made for Dorothy, Mary and Matthew on the split-log benches that had been pulled out from under the table. Dorothy had found that the best way to escape the unwanted attentions of Jansen and Mead was to make a show of moving closer to Anderson.

Anderson sat on his own bush-timber stool at one end, filling every inch of the extra space this seating arrangement gave him. His solid legs splayed, knees apart, and his huge shoulders were supported by both elbows resting on the table as he ate. Nurla and Biddi sat on one side of the fireplace, at the same end of the room, and at mealtimes Dorothy tried to position herself opposite them. Once, she had felt Anderson's eyes on her, but he had looked away quickly. This had been so unlike his normal fierce scrutiny that a strange thought had crossed her mind. Perhaps beneath all his ferocity there was a deep shyness.

Winterbourne, at the other end of the long table, looked weedy by comparison to Anderson. Nevertheless, since John Bathurst had left, Winterbourne had made it clear that the place opposite Anderson was now his. By what right, no one knew. And although Anderson made no objection, there was often an undercurrent of tension between them.

After the evening meal, there was no chance of tea, since the pot had not yet been cleaned. Dorothy and Mary were offered rum. Dorothy sipped hers indifferently, but Mary found the thick, sweet liquor slid easily down her throat.

26

IT WAS JUST BEFORE THE EVENING MEAL ONE NIGHT WHEN DOROTHY came upon Anderson washing himself at the well. She paused, not knowing what to do.

Anderson caught Dorothy by the arm and dragged her to one side. Her fists clenched automatically and she gasped.

'Beg pardon, Miss,' Anderson said, pointing. Dorothy looked down. There was a large spider on her dress. She laughed with relief and he laughed too. He brushed the spider from her hem, then he took her in his arms and kissed her on the mouth. She kissed him back.

From that point on, it was as if a wall of protection had been thrown around her. But Mary was suspicious and disapproving.

'I need his protection. You have Matthew!' Dorothy protested. Mary lowered her accusing eyes.

'He is loving, but he's not strong,' she confessed. 'Sometimes I reckon Jimmy is more a man than Matthew, although he's so much younger.'

Dorothy relented and hugged her sister. 'You know I'll always love ya.'

With her arms around Mary, Dorothy could not help noticing how little flesh was left on her. 'You must try and eat more, Mary, and ya got to stop drinking that poison,' she said, holding her by the shoulder and examining her closely. 'The food is good, when ya get used to it. Better than we had at the Sound.'

'I know, but I have this twist in my stomach when I have to sit at table with those . . . creatures. I'm afraid, Dolly. I'm afraid for all of us.'

Dorothy pulled her in close again and they rocked each other, both taking comfort from renewed affection, as they had always done after falling out.

'It'll come right,' Dorothy said. 'And when we're both old ladies we'll look back on it as a big adventure.'

During the long days when the sealers were away, Dorothy and Mary began to spend more time with the Aboriginal women in their bush camp, helping prepare food. Their other company was William Church. Knowing the circumstances of his departure from England and arrival at Swan River Colony made their own family situation seem somehow less desperate, their parents less gullible.

Meanwhile, the days were drawing in. Huge waves battered the tiny island, sometimes sending their chilling spray all the way to the top of the granite outcrop. Rain pelted the makeshift shelter and hut relentlessly for several days. Finally it forced its way in to the hut, dripping from the log-rafters and pooling on one end of the table.

Most of the sealers had already rolled themselves tightly

into their sealskin bedding under the veranda roof. Johnno remained, slumped forward on the table where he had fallen asleep between Winterbourne and William Church. Putting off leaving the comfort of the fire, Dorothy stood warming herself, watching the curtain in the storeroom doorway swelling into the kitchen as each gust of wind pushed through the gaps in the wooden shutters.

Anderson, who had been staring into his mug, suddenly drained his drink, rose from his seat and held out his hand to Dorothy. She stood still, searching his black eyes. They gave nothing away. His chin was raised and his thick lips, although not smiling, seemed fuller, less restrained. He made no move towards her this time, but waited, watching through half-closed eyes, for her to decide. She felt herself take a step towards him. Drawn irrevocably forward, she went with him into his private quarters.

The room was dark and smelled of leather, gunmetal and dust. As her eyes adjusted, she saw that the bed was a pile of skins. Anderson's musket stood against the wall.

Anderson took off his cloak and unbuckled the belt that held the pistols. He placed them beside the musket and moved towards her. She stood her ground while he caressed her. She fought to keep her breathing steady. As his arm circled her waist and drew her to him, she closed her eyes.

The next day, the rain was squally, but not so constant. When Matthew and Mary did not appear for breakfast, Dorothy went to see how they had fared in the shelter.

'How could ya do it!' Mary flew at her sister and beat her

fists against her chest as if they were still children fighting over the same toy. Dorothy's head went up defiantly even as she rejoiced in the fact that Mary was showing some spirit at last. Matthew quickly vacated the shelter to escape the warring women.

'We'll all be safer if I'm with him than if I'm not,' Dorothy said fiercely, grabbing Mary's flailing arms and holding them away from her body.

'Safer!' Mary, her energy expended, sat down heavily.

'Yes! You, Jimmy, even your precious Matthew,' Dorothy said, buoyed by anger.

'Matthew is a good man,' Mary defended her husband. 'At least I know he'll not murder me in my bed.'

'Murder ya!' Dorothy was horrified.

'Well, everyone knows what an animal Anderson is when he's roused,' Mary explained.

'Do they so?' Dorothy smiled at her sister, whose eyes widened. Then they both giggled.

Later in the day, as Dorothy approached Nurla and Biddi's humpy, she saw Johnno enter with a dozen or so fresh whiting tied together and dangling by their tails.

Nurla took the fish from Johnno, carried them to the garden and hung them over the brushwood fence. Biddi picked up a bucket and headed towards the well.

As Nurla slit the smooth white belly of each fish with her knife, blood and guts spilled out onto the garden soil. When all the fish had been cleaned, Nurla used her digging stick to bury the entrails.

Biddi returned and sluiced out the innards. Dorothy helped to carry the fish back to the humpy.

Sitting cross-legged on the ground and balancing shallow wooden bowls on their knees, Nurla and Biddi began to scrape away the stiff, silver scales. Dorothy picked up a fish and tried to copy their actions.

'Do you miss your people?' she asked as she scraped the fish uncertainly.

'Me missus,' Biddi corrected, pointing to herself.

'No, I mean, are you sad?'

Nurla raised her eyes from the task, then turned to look more directly at Biddi than she ever did at Dorothy. 'Sad when baby die,' she said softly. 'Sad inside.' Nurla folded her body as if in pain.

'Oh.' Dorothy glanced from one to the other. When both women remained silent she asked, 'How old was the baby?' Biddi frowned with concentration and studied the fish in her hand.

'My brothers died – when they were babies,' Dorothy added, not knowing how much the women understood. But they both began to nod, their bodies rocking slowly in time with their heads.

'Longtime sad inside.'

Dorothy felt an unexpected pang of jealousy, wondering if the baby had been Anderson's and whether he had been sad, too.

She was discovering a softer side to the big American – one that he kept well hidden from his men. Perhaps he felt able to let down his guard with her, since Dorothy would never be a threat to his authority. Perhaps, having relaxed a little, he found the sensation to his liking. He had, after all, been living by his wits for nearly ten years, never allowing himself to get too close to anyone, even Bathurst. While he used his body with reckless abandon, fearing nothing in a physical sense, his emotions had been carefully guarded against the deeper pain of loss. A pain that he had known very early in his life and felt more keenly than torn flesh or broken bones.

Dorothy added her fish to the others', then scrubbed her hands with sand and water.

A few days later, Anderson gave Dorothy three valuable seal-skins as a gift. Two of the skins he softened with water. Then, following his instructions, Dorothy stood with one foot on the fur side of each while he knelt in front of her, moulding them around her feet and lacing the skins with stripped vines to make boots. The tightly curling black hair on his head came within reach of her hand. She touched it lightly.

'Winter be cold in these parts, Miss,' he said, looking up at her. Then, rising quickly, he moved away to pick up the third and largest skin. When he had trimmed the natural holes left by the seal's flippers, he held the skin up like a coat. Dorothy put her arms through the holes and wore the sleeveless garment over her dress.

27

AS ALWAYS, ANDERSON ROSE AT FIRST LIGHT, WENT TO THE WINDOW and flung open the wooden shutters. The morning sky was grey and sullen, with clouds piled thickly. There was no wind. The birds, usually so vocal at daybreak, seemed strangely silent.

He dressed quickly. With his pistols in place at his waist, he pushed aside the skins that hung in the doorway. The main room was deserted. Then his sharp eyes took in the veranda, the clearing, the surrounding scrub.

'Iie-zz-aaac!' Anderson's voice shattered the stillness.

Winterbourne's stiff hair and sallow face appeared from the bush where he had been relieving himself after a night's sleep.

'There be a foul smell of treachery ridin' the wind.'

'Must have snuck off during the night,' Winterbourne said, shaking his head.

'From under yo' nose?' Anderson glared at him.

'Wasn't me as was holed up all night with a fancy woman,' Winterbourne said slyly, shifting his shoulders as if to get rid of the blame.

Woken by the shouting, the other men began to rise.

'Where's Jansen?' James Manning threw off his bedding and rubbed his eyes.

'And the rest of them?' Gimble sat up and looked around.

'Gone,' Winterbourne said.

'Gone where?' Anderson viewed him with renewed suspicion. The Englishman shrugged.

'If I find out you had a hand in this . . .' Anderson grabbed a fistful of the sealskin vest that Winterbourne wore over his tattered shirt and dragged the smaller man up close to his face, '. . . you a dead man!' As he spat out the words, drops of saliva flew and landed on Winterbourne. Struggling free of Anderson's grasp, he brushed them off disdainfully. He would not meet Anderson's eyes. Black Jack shoved him away, turned on his heel and stormed back into the hut. In the storeroom, his fears were confirmed. Flour, rum and salt were missing.

Dorothy stayed out of Anderson's way, busying herself with the fire, mixing some of the remaining flour into damper and placing it in the coals. She didn't dare go to the shelter. She had heard James Manning's voice, which probably meant that Jimmy was also still there. In the last month, he had become inseparable from Manning, following him around like a lost puppy, in spite of Gimble's advice.

Mead came back from the beach with confirmation that the *Mountaineer*'s whaleboat was missing.

'But we'll catch 'em . . .' Mead scooped up cold stew from the pot and shoved it into his mouth '. . . and when we do we'll slit their throats! Look sharp, me hearties!' he cried in eager anticipation of the chase.

'Let them go,' Anderson growled.

The men looked astounded.

'Arrr, you know Jansen,' Mead protested. 'His tongue will wag the minute he hits the Sound.'

'Nothin' surer,' Hill agreed.

'And not only him, there's the others,' Gimble added.

'Belay there!' Anderson shouted. 'We won't be wastin' time or effort on scum like that.' He walked out into the clearing and the subject was closed.

Mary and Matthew had still not appeared. They must have heard all the commotion. Matthew, at least, would have looked out to see what was going on – unless he already knew. Either he was lying low, or had gone with Jansen.

Nurla and Biddi came up from their camp. Anderson ordered a head count. Jansen, Evans and Paine were missing. Dorothy raised worried eyes to Jimmy, who finally went to examine the shelter. When he returned, she saw by the look on his face that it was vacated.

Although she was shocked and hurt by the fact that Mary had gone without saying goodbye, Dorothy could not help worrying about her sister, whose life was once again at the mercy of the elements and the despised Captain Jansen. But she could not risk asking Anderson to intervene. She felt that a genuine affection had grown up between herself and Anderson. But with the second whaleboat gone, he would be in no mood to tolerate any hint of disloyalty. Dorothy would have to be careful. She also knew, perhaps better than he did, just how precarious his position had become. With Winterbourne showing more blatant ambition and Manning sulking in corners, it was difficult enough to maintain harmony in the camp. Anderson had spoken of the companionship and steadying influence of his friend, Bathurst. Dorothy would have to try and fill that void.

The loss of income that the second whaleboat had provided did not improve any of the men's tempers. And the defection of the ageing Henry Paine had a sobering effect on them all.

As the days passed, James Manning became openly argumentative. He complained of being constantly wet, stinking and tired. In fact, he was bored with the isolation of Middle Island and sick of the hard, physical work of sealing. Like Matthew Gill, he had ambitions of becoming a landowner and gentleman. If he had heard even a whisper of Jansen's intention to leave, he would have somehow wormed his way in to the party. But they had gone without him, silently, under cover of darkness. He felt cheated and abandoned once again.

Since it would be more than his life was worth to express any of this to the edgy Anderson, he confided in Jimmy Newell. Always more inclined to trust people than not, Jimmy felt important – here was an educated and civilised man, who seemed to value him as a companion. But when he boasted to Dorothy of this new friendship, she was quick to warn him.

'He uses ya, Jimmy. Can ya not see that?'

'Arr, Dolly, will ya stop your naggin'? I ain't little Jimmy no more.' He stepped up beside her to measure his height and laughed when she had to tilt her head back to look at him. She was sure that he had grown several inches since they had been on the island. Certainly the regular meals had put flesh on his large frame. 'And you and me, we both know what Father would say about *him*,' Jimmy teased, looking across the clearing to where Anderson was supervising repairs to the whaleboat.

'Cheeky sod.' Dorothy smiled and gave her brother a good-natured shove.

'Things is different here, eh?' he said, still grinning.

While Anderson withdrew more and more to his private quarters, Winterbourne was everywhere. Sneering at Johnno, kicking Jimmy or Manning, arguing with Gimble. But with Mead and Hill he talked in low tones, looking over his shoulder constantly to make sure they were not overheard.

Often in the nights that followed, Dorothy would wake and find that Anderson was not beside her. Sometimes, he stood with the shutters thrown open, looking and listening into the darkness. At other times, the closed room would have a cold emptiness about it and she would get up, wrap her shawl around her and go out to the veranda where the men slept.

One night, she found Anderson standing on the ridge that overlooked the bay, a lone figure that could have been carved in stone except that the fur of his cloak was ruffled by the wind. He made no move as she came up beside him, and they stood together for several minutes before she spoke.

'Do ya hear somethin' amiss?' Dorothy asked at last.

'I hear many things, day and night.'

'Voices?'

'Voices, footsteps, gunshots.' He turned away from the sea. 'I wonder if it ain't all in my head.' He walked so fast along the sandy track that she had to run to keep up with him. Reminded of her presence by the sound of her breathing, he glanced down. 'The tide is on the turn,' he said.

28

IT WAS CLOSE TO MIDDAY. SMOKE ROSE IN A WHITE PLUME FROM
the kiln where Nurla was boiling down blubber in the trypot. William Church was writing. Dorothy sat watching
the banded lizards darting about, competing for insects and
soaking up warmth in the sundrenched clearing.

Suddenly, there were voices.

'Are they back so soon?' Startled, Dorothy and Church
looked at each other, then stood up.

Winterbourne came up from the beach, an angry scowl on
his face.

'You're back early,' Dorothy said.

'Stupid boy!' Winterbourne snapped. 'Should have shoved
him overboard and saved the oar.' He sat down on one of the
flat rocks next to the camp fire in the clearing, picked up a
stout stick and began to poke around amongst the charred
wood and ash.

In ones and twos the other sealers straggled up from the
beach, until everyone had arrived except Anderson and Gimble. When Dorothy asked where they were, Jimmy told her
they had work to do. She went to find them.

From the ridge, she saw Gimble whittling away with his sealing knife at a short piece of wood. A wattle pole, recently cut, lay on the sand while Anderson stripped leaves from several lengths of trailing vine. This tough, flexible vine grew profusely on the island and was used for all manner of repairs. She decided not to disturb the men and followed the ridge to the next bay where she gathered some leathery sea-sponges that had washed up on the rocks.

It wasn't until after the evening meal that she heard the full story.

'There it was leapin' out of the water. I swear it was wantin' to join us in the boat!' Now that the shock of the actual event had worn off, Gimble was ready to elaborate. He went on to tell how on their way out to Finger Island they had seen a group of sharks. Although they had lost sight of them before they reached the island, the men had kept a more vigilant lookout than usual while Biddi herded seals.

Their first catch was small and they wondered if the sharks had beaten them to it. Then, as they loaded the Beetle, their troubles began.

As he heaved a heavy seal carcass onto the gunwale, Manning carelessly allowed blood to run down the side of the hull and into the water. By the time the boat was half a mile out to sea, the sharks were circling.

Anderson gave the order to heave-to and they sat for some time quietly rocking in the water, making as little disturbance as possible in the hope that the sharks would lose interest. Then the wind sprang up, making the water opaque and choppy. The sharks were still there. One in particular circled closer, its battle-scarred fin slicing the surface. When it nudged the hull, Anderson decided that they would have to move on.

They raised the sail, but before they could get under way the shark leapt out of the water. For a long moment it towered over the boat. Its tiny eyes looked straight at the men before it rose above them. As its white underbelly sank back into the sea it opened its huge mouth and latched on to Manning's oar.

Everyone was shouting. Manning was wrenched to his feet, but held on, jerking the oar to try and dislodge the shark. But its razor-sharp teeth were imbedded deep in the wood.

'Aye, nearly had us all feedin' those monsters,' Hill added. 'The old Beetle pitched so far over . . .' But it was Gimble's story and he glared at Hill.

'I gave that shark a good thump with me own oar. But those teeth! Ya've never seen the like, I'll wager,' Gimble said.

'It's a good long time since you saw the like of *any* teeth, you old goat,' said Hill, determined not to be disregarded. Gimble pulled back his lips and pointed to his one remaining tooth. Amid the laughter there were cries of 'That ain't teeth,' and 'How much will ya wager?'

But the oar and the chance of more seals were lost when Anderson decided to make use of the wind and head for home while they could.

'Should'a finished what we started. Missed a good day's catch there.' Winterbourne was grumbling again.

Anderson moved towards Winterbourne. His voice was low, but there was a dangerous glint in his eyes.

'Was you plannin' to dip yo' oar on both sides of that boat when the wind died?'

'Maybe,' Winterbourne replied haughtily. 'But what about our profits? Make Manning pay, I say.'

'You a greedy sod.' Anderson scowled in the Englishman's face.

'Yeah, and you're goin' soft in your old age,' Winterbourne retorted. Jerking free, he slipped away from Anderson's grasp. There was a sharp intake of breath from the others. Delivered as it was in front of witnesses, this was a blatant challenge to Anderson's authority. They had seen men killed for less. Anderson drew one of his pistols. He gripped Winterbourne's shoulder and held the gun at his temple.

'If I be gettin' soft, then you in luck, man,' Anderson told him. 'But don't go bettin' on it.'

The next day most of the crew lounged around the clearing. As if to mock their idleness, the sky remained blue, the winds light. But until he was satisfied with the new oar, Anderson would not take the boat out. Late in the afternoon, Gimble came up from the beach.

'Oar's mended,' he said.

'About time.' Winterbourne had just rejoined the men in the clearing. There was soil under his fingernails. This was unusual since he was always making a big show of sharpening his knife, then cleaning his fingernails with the point.

'What's eating him?' Jimmy asked Gimble as he picked up the buckets and headed for the well.

'Rattle me ro'locks, I'll swear he has his fair share of

everythin' and still reckons he's hard done by,' Gimble explained as he threw an unused piece of vine on the fire. 'But sure 'tis no time at all since he and Mead joined the crew. Old hands like me and Anderson, well, we've a stash put by . . . retirement fund, ya might say. But hard won for all that.'

29

DRAWN FURTHER FROM MIDDLE ISLAND AS THE SEASON PROGRESSED and mature seals became less plentiful, Anderson and his men landed, just after sunset, to spend the night in a sheltered bay on the island they called North Twin Peak. To their great surprise, they heard the sounds of laughter and raised human voices. Quietly beaching their boat, they discussed the possibility of Jansen and his party having taken shelter in another bay, since this was one of the larger islands in the archipelago between Middle Island and King George Sound.

'If it be so, then Jansen be mine,' Anderson said darkly.

'Whoever it is they've been on the grog,' Gimble commented.

Anderson sent Manning, who was the best bushman among the crew, to investigate. Jimmy made a move to go with him.

'Not you, boy,' Anderson said. Jimmy ducked his head as if to avoid a blow, and regarded Anderson from the corner of one eye. 'An elephant could move with more stealth,' the big man told him. Since Jimmy's fear of Anderson outweighed his devotion to Manning, he made no further attempt to follow.

Half an hour later, Manning returned to report a group of strangers, probably sealers, camped in the next bay. The strong southerly wind was keeping the smoke from their fire low and sweeping it away to the north, so that Anderson had neither seen nor smelt it as he brought his boat in from the south-east.

'Five men,' Manning said, 'drinking whiskey. They've a whole crate of flagons on the beach.'

'Whiskey, eh?' Anderson's face relaxed into a crooked grin. 'Ain't no harm in payin' a social visit.'

There were murmurs of surprise and muffled enthusiasm. Anderson was always careful not to reveal his whereabouts unless it was absolutely necessary. But this was a rare opportunity to drink whiskey.

Manning led the way while Winterbourne and Gimble walked on either side of Anderson. The others bunched up behind as they crossed the ridge between the two bays and soon came upon the sealers.

The empty shells of sand crabs and scallops were scattered around the fire. A whiskey flagon passed from hand to hand, the men drinking from it in turns and protesting loudly if it stayed in one place for too long. The first man to look up and see the giant figure of Anderson standing on the ridge above let out a yelp of fear. All heads turned towards the new arrivals.

'Nice drop o' whiskey you got there, man,' Anderson said, bearing down on the stunned group.

'Don't mind if we do.' Winterbourne followed, but turned aside to lift an unopened flagon from the nearby crate.

'Hoy! Put that down, you thievin' bastard!' The closest of the strangers leapt to his feet. In an instant, Winterbourne's knife had slashed the skin on the man's neck and drawn blood. Anderson spun around and loomed over the pair.

'Avast there,' he said as he grabbed Winterbourne's wrist. The razor-sharp blade fell from Winterbourne's hand and sliced into his sealskin boot. With the point of his own knife still stuck in his foot, Winterbourne danced and hobbled while the men around the fire laughed heartily. Their own injured man had scuttled back to his mates where the blood was being staunched with a grubby bandana.

Having removed the knife and examined the flesh wound in his foot, Winterbourne confronted Anderson. 'Your arm is long, but my memory is longer,' he hissed up into the big man's face.

'And my temper grows perilous short in a fool's company.' Anderson's voice rumbled, and he looked ready to send Winterbourne sprawling, but changed his mind. Dropping his voice, he spoke through gritted teeth. 'There be more to gain here than whiskey if we play our cards right.'

Anderson turned his back on Winterbourne and spoke to the group around the fire. 'We ain't lookin' for no trouble, just company. I see you got a game goin' there.' He pointed to the cards still held by some of the men. 'We play for the whiskey – winner takes all.'

There were loud protests from the keepers of the whiskey about having bought it fair and square. But Anderson knew it was much more likely that they had been delivering a consignment to the soldiers in King George Sound and had quietly kept one crate back for themselves. 'I can't say fairer than that now,' Anderson insisted. 'Deal us in.' He beckoned to the rest of his men.

The sealers around the fire could see that they were out-numbered and pooled the cards in readiness for a new game.

With the Middle Island crew gathered around him, Ander-son said quietly, 'Drink and pass, men, but go easy. They've bin at it a while. There be a rich haul for us and no bodies to bury, if we stay on the sober side.' He indicated the pile of skins just visible in the boat that was beached on the sand.

The two groups mingled, warily eyeing each other at first, then becoming more friendly as the whiskey warmed and soothed them. Anderson's men appeared to drink as deeply as the others and became just as rowdy and unsteady of hand. Anderson and Gimble quickly accumulated a pile of wooden chips. But Winterbourne was still fuming after the humiliat-ing spat with Anderson and muttered to Mead, 'What are we playin' games for? Time was when we'd a had their guts for fish-bait.'

When Anderson indicated the drunken men already fall-ing asleep around the fire, a different look finally came into Winterbourne's eyes. Anderson, Winterbourne and Gimble kept playing with the remaining strangers, passing the flagon around the group, while Hill, Mead, Jimmy and Manning stretched out and pretended to be sleeping. One by one, the strangers fell into a drunken stupor. At about midnight, Anderson signalled to his men and they made off back to their own boat with the remaining whiskey and all of the sealskins.

'By the time they recover from that hangover they won't remember anything,' Manning said, pleased to have gained a dozen extra skins without having to do the gruelling work.

'Pity there was no gold on 'em,' Winterbourne remarked, drawing a finger across his throat to show what he would have done to get it.

Over the next few weeks, winter set in. Instead of moving outside to lounge around in the open clearing after dinner, the sealers stayed longer by the fire inside the hut. Sitting on the split-log benches at the table, they drank their rum, played cards and told their stories of daring and danger with rough humour and grudging compassion.

Manning's frustration at the thought of another winter spent on Middle Island made him more vocal than ever in his complaints, muttering to anyone who would listen that he was being held against his will.

'Be off then, you lily-livered codfish,' Anderson roared.

'Ya'd make a tasty meal for yon sharks, lad.' Gimble laughed at the absurdity of the young man's accusation. He had plenty of food, alcohol, shelter and company. What more could he want?

In milder weather, Winterbourne had managed to hold sway around the outside camp fire by flashing his knife and claiming that Anderson had put him in charge.

The move inside forced Winterbourne to operate under Anderson's eye. Usually, he was careful to at least give lip service to the big American's position as leader of the group. But there were times when, because he was drunk or particularly frustrated, this veneer of respect slipped.

During one of these evenings, Winterbourne's resentment of Johnno bubbled to the surface.

'Said they'd come back,' Winterbourne said. 'But they didn't, did they, Johnno?' The eyes of the young man in question darted around the group, trying to gauge whether this was a joke or not. 'Ate nothin' but raw penguin for a year, so he says.' Winterbourne's snigger became a reckless laugh, but none of Anderson's men joined in. Seeking out the faces of Mead and Hill, he moved closer to Johnno and jabbed him in the chest with one finger. 'You know I've never eaten a penguin. Neither, I'll wager, have our shipmates here. So why don't we take you back to your island, eh? You can catch a couple of birds and show us how it's done, like.'

These words were delivered with such cutting sarcasm that Johnno's body began to tremble and a whimper escaped his throat. Anderson, who had been engrossed in his card game, lifted his head. A hush descended on the other sealers as the big man's chin thrust dangerously forward. But Winterbourne either didn't notice or decided to ignore it.

'About time he earned his keep, wouldn't ya say, lads?' His shifty eyes fastened on Johnno for a long moment before he swung his gaze around the room, checking for allies.

'Leave it,' Anderson said, his eyes narrowing to slits. Except for Mead and Hill who looked down and appeared to be almost as uncomfortable as Johnno, the men watched Anderson as they would a wild animal about to pounce. But Winterbourne wasn't finished yet.

'No work, no food. Them's the rules. Equal shares of every-thin'. I'm not mistaken, am I, lads?' There was still a touch of banter in the Englishman's voice, but the fixed smile on his face held no trace of humour. Anderson rose to his feet.

'Equal shares?' he said. The men whose heads had been lowered could no longer avoid being involved and looked up as Anderson's black eyes made contact with everyone in the room. 'You be first then, Isaac.' Winterbourne's eyebrows lifted in expectation. 'We can leave you off on that rock tomorrow . . . for a year, maybe . . . same as Johnno.'

The men broke into laughter. 'Yeah, fair's fair,' they said, clicking their mugs together and resuming their own conversations. Winterbourne's expression quickly changed. Even the men who had tried to remain neutral now joined in the mirth. But Anderson didn't laugh.

30

WINTER STORMS HAD GIVEN WAY TO FINER, DRYER WEATHER. WITH
spring approaching, the sealers once again built their camp
fire in the clearing and gathered around it. Or perhaps an
increasing atmosphere of tension in the hut had driven them
out. Sitting on the flat rocks or lounging full length on the
ground, supported on one elbow, they smoked their pipes,
but the usual good-natured ribbing and loud boasting that
had characterised these gatherings in the past was strangely
muted.

As the light faded one evening, Johnno took the tin whistle
from his belt and began to play. It was a slow, melancholy tune.
Thin, reedy notes drifted and mingled with the smoke rising
into the evening air. No one had ventured into the kitchen,
although it was past the usual time for the evening meal.

Anderson appeared in the doorway of the hut and stood
listening. Johnno glanced in his direction and suddenly the
tempo of the music changed. The notes streamed fuller and
faster from the thin whistle until they became a familiar tune.
Heads turned towards Johnno, feet started to tap. Anderson slapped one hand against his thigh in time to the music.

William Church and Dorothy were drawn out to the veranda by the rousing sounds of the hornpipe.

Unable to resist the music for long, Nimble Gimble was, as usual, the first to be up on his feet. But the others quickly joined him, their gap-toothed grins in the flickering firelight giving them a fierce, ghoulish appearance. The whoops and hollers they emitted as the dance gathered momentum could easily have been mistaken for war cries. But the louder and more blood-curdling their voices, the happier the men became. With their arms across each other's shoulders, they hopped and stamped together, heads frequently thrown back with laughter then forward again to keep balance and avoid the tangling of legs and feet.

Dorothy found that she was also clapping in time with the music. Then, smiling up at Anderson, she took his hand and tried to draw him out into the clearing. At first he resisted, almost shyly. Then he grabbed her by the waist and whirled her with him into the open space between the veranda and the dancing men.

With arms outstretched and hands on each other's hips, they danced, sidestepping together this way and that, sometimes the length of the veranda and back again, sometimes around in a circle.

The music continued, louder, faster. The other dancers stopped to watch. They clapped the rhythm as Dorothy's skirts swirled and Anderson leapt from one foot to the other in time with the beat. Between bouts of fierce concentration, a slightly embarrassed grin appeared on his face.

Finally exhausted, Dorothy dropped her arms to her sides

and doubled over, laughing and gasping for air. Surprised by her own audacity, she caught her breath and straightened up, her breasts still heaving. Anderson was equally surprised at how such a thing could happen. But, led by Gimble, the men were applauding and shouting their approval. Dorothy turned away from Anderson to bow in their direction. She had never learned to curtsey. When she looked again at Anderson he was offering his arm. He waved it uncertainly out from his body and back again as if this sort of gesture was totally foreign to him. Dorothy slipped her arm through his and together they led the men into the warm kitchen where steam was rising from the brimming pot.

At daybreak, Anderson roused the men, nudging them with the toe of his sealskin boot. They rolled out reluctantly, grumbling about the cold and the early start, but secretly happy to be going to sea again.

William Church teased Dorothy about her dancing, but declared it to be just the sort of distraction that everyone, with the exception of Winterbourne, needed. Church had seen him disappear into the shadows around the back of the hut and noticed that he didn't reappear until the others were eating.

'What's he up to?' Dorothy asked.

'No good. You can be sure of that,' Church said quietly.

Dorothy studied his frowning face. 'So you don't trust him either?' she said. But William Church would say nothing more.

From the kitchen, the smell of warm damper wafted into

the air. Always acutely aware of his privileged position, William Church had developed an uncanny knack of anticipating Anderson's mood and movements. He had already heated water for tea in several pannikins and had swung the pot with the remains of last night's meal back onto the fire. The sealers filed through the room, each taking a piece of damper, scooping up the juices from the pot and washing their food down with the scalding tea. There was no time for sitting at the table. When Anderson said the boat was going out, he meant now! Anyone who was not on board would not only incur Anderson's wrath, but forfeit his share of the skins taken that day. And, if Anderson was still in a foul mood when they returned, he might even turn a blind eye while Winterbourne administered his own rough justice.

Sometimes the offender gave as good as he got, drawing his own sealing knife and standing up to Winterbourne. But although Winterbourne was a physical coward, he was devious and patient. The offender would more than likely find his bedroll contaminated with faeces of unknown origin, or his mug missing so that he had to beg one of the others to share their rum with him after the evening meal.

Once the sealers had gone, William Church would eat with Johnno before they went about their various chores. Church gathered firewood and stoked the fire. On days when he was well enough, Johnno went out in the boat. Other days, he stayed to keep watch from the ridge in case there was a likely-looking ship to report to Anderson.

Dorothy walked. Coming back from her walk that day, she saw Biddi at the edge of the lake. She was working on the skins, scraping away the fat with a flat stone and rubbing in salt.

'Morning,' Dorothy called.

'Mornin', missus,' Biddi mumbled, barely looking up from her task. She paused to watch as Biddi's hands moved skilfully over the skins, checking for tears or discolouration. After a few minutes, Biddi glanced up again.

'Hard work, Biddi?' Dorothy asked. The other woman nodded.

'Work hard, eat good tucker,' she said. 'Not like my country.'

'Tell me about your country, Biddi.'

'Can't remember,' Biddi said, quickly dropping her eyes and closing the conversation.

After her walk, Dorothy was always hungry. She ate the damper Church had saved for her, then tidied the hut, sweeping the dirt floor with a brushwood broom. As she worked, Church wrote in his notebook.

'Do you write about me?' Dorothy asked him, sweeping around his feet.

'I write about everyone . . . everything.'

'Why?'

'So that others do not suffer as we have done.'

'But who will read what you write?'

'That I do not know, but someone must. We were cruelly deceived by those in authority at Swan River Colony and King George Sound. If these things are not reported, more innocent lives will be ruined. I am making a complete copy so that, if anything happens to me . . .'

Dorothy stared at him, wanting to say that nothing would happen, that they were safe here, well fed and sheltered. But then she thought of Anderson prowling in the night, hearing voices. Perhaps even he was not invincible.

Her mind wandered back to King George Sound. Little William had been in her thoughts a lot lately. As had Biddi's baby who died, and her own infant brothers in England. She wondered if Netty was really up to the task of caring for the young ones. And what of her mother, and Mary? Were they together now? Had Jansen's whaleboat arrived at the Sound, or had they been picked up by a passing ship and taken somewhere else? With more time on her hands now that sealing had begun again in earnest, Dorothy was frequently plagued by such thoughts.

Anderson looked up from his meal that evening, examining Dorothy's face with his inscrutable black eyes. She had grown more beautiful as the months had passed. The trauma of the shipwreck had faded. With regular meals her face had filled out, smoothing away the lines on her forehead and adding a healthy glow to her skin. But he knew she was missing her family and longing for news.

Anderson was conscious, too, that, while basic supplies were running low, sealskins were piling higher on the floor of the storeroom. It would make sense to take them in to the trading post. Passing ships were often short of supplies themselves and no amount of threats or murderous beatings could produce what was not on board.

31

Half hidden in a patch of wattle scrub, James Manning could be seen shouting up into the face of Anderson, who towered over him, glowering.

'You've stolen my money!' Manning yelled, flapping his threadbare jacket to show the damaged lining.

'I ain't got yo' money, boy,' Anderson said, looking like a giant about to swat a fly.

'That's a lie! I saw you counting it!' Manning insisted.

'Forty-six pounds?' Anderson laughed. 'Why would I lift such a piddlin' sum?'

'Because you are a pirate and a blaggard!' Manning yelled. In an instant, Anderson's pistol was pointed at Manning's head. Beyond caution or reason, Manning pushed the muzzle aside. 'What's more, you keep me here with false promises, treat me with contempt and force me to work at your filthy trade. All for the privilege of eating swill and sleeping rough! Now you steal all that I have left!'

Anderson lowered the pistol and drew his knife, but his mouth curled up in a half smile, perhaps at the audacity of this young upstart. Winterbourne appeared in the same patch of scrub. He drew his sealing knife and made a show of protecting Anderson. The other men stood about uneasily, their hands not far from their own knives. Winterbourne took a menacing step towards Manning, brandishing the knife close to his face.

'Hold ya tongue, ya worthless eel, or ya'll find it fed to the crows.' Winterbourne's shirt looked as if it had been hastily tucked in to his trousers. He raised his arm and the bulge of a money belt became obvious beneath his clothes. Manning stood his ground.

'I'd trust the crows sooner than any one of you,' he said. His eyes flicked around the group of sealers before returning to Anderson. 'I have kept my side of the bargain. God knows I have worked for my keep, which you have continued to take from my share of the skins. But I see that you have no intention of keeping *your* promise to take me to King George Sound.'

'I ain't made no promise,' Anderson declared.

'I demand that you give back my money. How else am I to pay for my passage on any decent ship?' Manning shouted at Anderson, who stood, hands on hips, chin raised. He appeared to look over Manning's head, as if he had more important things on his mind than this sordid argument. But anyone who thought that his slitted eyes did not take in everything around him would be making a grave mistake.

'I never took yo' money,' Anderson said, and sheathed his knife. With the pistol already back in his belt, he turned and walked away.

In extreme frustration, Manning shouted, 'Damn you, Anderson! Put me ashore and I'll walk!'

Expressions of disbelief, even amusement, rippled through the group of men. Someone laughed out loud. Winterbourne disappeared into the hut. Anderson's eyes followed him before returning to Manning.

'As you wish,' he said quietly.

There were sharp intakes of breath as the pirates looked at each other. Although the words themselves were mild, there was no mistaking Anderson's resolve. Manning paused for barely a second. If he was taken aback, he managed to conceal the fact, as if not wanting to give Anderson the slightest satisfaction.

'When?' he demanded.

'Now!' Anderson turned abruptly, his huge frame suddenly animated, radiating heat and power. 'Gimble, Mead, Hill,' he signalled his men to the beached boat. 'Where's Isaac?'

Winterbourne appeared in the doorway of the hut, his clothing neatly rearranged. As Manning collected his swag, Jimmy Newell did the same.

'What are you doing?' Manning asked him.

'Comin' with ya,' Jimmy said.

Manning looked around at the other men. Events were moving too fast. He needed time to think. His pride would not allow him to back down, but if someone else would speak out against the notion . . .

The faces were impassive, the voices silent in response to his mute appeal.

'Suit yourself,' Manning said at last, hoisting his bedroll onto his shoulder and setting off for the beach. Jimmy followed.

Watching her brother in disbelief, Dorothy ran to him, and caught at his arm. 'Jimmy, are ya mad? This is nowt to do with ya!'

'Let us go, Dolly,' Jimmy said quietly.

She released him. Her arms flopped at her sides as he moved away. At the edge of the clearing, she ran up close behind him again. He looked over his shoulder, but kept walking.

'You'll come back?' she called.

'I'll send a ship,' Jimmy mouthed the words and strode away. Dorothy ran back to the storeroom, found a tinderbox, and raced back to the beach, where she was just able to hand it slyly to Jimmy before the boat moved out over the first set of waves.

In the whaleboat, not one word was spoken until they touched the beach at Cape Arid. In the shallows, Anderson thrust the steering oar deep into the sand to hold the boat steady while Manning and Jimmy stepped out into the lapping waves.

Manning was agitated. With his anger spent, he was beginning to waver, to regret this hasty, ill-planned departure. Jimmy stood beside him. Anderson, unmoved and silent as a tree trunk, towered in the stern of the boat.

Manning looked up at Anderson.

Anderson lifted the steering oar. The boat floated free.

'You can't leave us here!' Manning shouted. Gimble, who sat at one of the forward oars, bent his back and pulled away with the others.

James Manning and Jimmy Newell stood on the deserted shore, 400 miles from King George Sound, with their sealing knives, their bedrolls and Dorothy's gift.

32

DOROTHY HAD KEPT WATCH FROM THE RIDGE ABOVE THE BEACH, but her hopes of seeing her brother's stocky figure in the returning boat had been dashed. Anderson came striding up the path.

'What happened? Where's Jimmy?' she asked anxiously. When Anderson did not reply, she leapt at him, beating with her fists, raining blows on the hard muscles of his chest and stomach. He stood still, receiving her blows.

'Talk to me!' Dorothy cried at last, standing back, hands on hips. 'Tell me ya didn't go and leave my little brother on some desolate beach with that stupid Manning!' Anderson flinched.

'His course was set,' he said at last. 'There weren't no stoppin' him.'

Dorothy turned away.

Running and stumbling in her sealskin boots, she left the path. Tears blurred her vision. Bushes whipped her, catching at her clothes and grazing her skin. On top of the ridge, the wind hit her hard in the face. Pushing on through the scrub, she reached the northernmost point of the island.

Then, squaring her shoulders and lifting her chin, she stood staring out across the narrow but impassable stretch of water to where her brother – her clumsy, laughing, teasing brother – had been abandoned to his fate.

Anderson was particularly quiet that night. He sat bent over his food, scooping it quickly into his mouth, and washing it down with drafts of rum, and retired early to his room without a word.

When Dorothy joined him later, after clearing and sweeping out the kitchen, he was lying in bed with the musket at his side. His eyes opened as she entered and he watched her undress and climb in between the skins. Dorothy settled herself beside him and allowed the warmth of his body to seep into her own.

'He'd a mind to go,' Anderson said.

'I know,' Dorothy murmured. 'He was always stubborn. And he would not leave Manning to walk alone.' There was a pause in which they lay silently together. 'Will they reach the Sound?'

Anderson grunted. 'Manning got what was comin' to him. But Jimmy . . . he should have come back with us . . . once he seen the lie o' the land.'

There was distress in Anderson's voice. He felt a rare sense of confusion. Things that he had known with such certainty before no longer seemed clear. He was grappling with emotions he had never felt, or had pushed so far down that he no longer recognised them.

'Jimmy's a strong boy,' Dorothy said at last. 'And growin''

up fast.' She tried to sound convincing, for her own sake as much as Anderson's. But neither of them got much sleep that night.

33

'YOU HAVEN'T SEEN THE LAST OF ME, YOU BLACK-HEARTED BASTARD!' Manning had shouted as the whaleboat pulled away. But his voice was blown back into his own ears by the cold wind that came up from the south.

While he was flattered by Jimmy's loyalty, Manning worried that he would now have to find food for both of them. Not only had that unscrupulous pirate stolen his money, he had abandoned him – left him to die. To make matters worse, he was now saddled with this overgrown kid, Jimmy Newell, who obviously knew nothing about living off the land, either here or back in the old country. A roof thatcher! What use was that when your belly was rumbling and your throat was parched? Manning's own survival skills had been honed by the eight years he had spent marooned, first on Kangaroo Island, then on Middle Island. His earlier life in Sydney Cove, when he himself had been as raw and naive as Jimmy, now seemed to have belonged to someone else.

Brought up in a strictly religious family, Manning's sense of right and wrong had been sorely tested and reshaped by his experiences. 'Every man for himself' had become his new code of ethics in the desperate fight for survival, but he could never quite bring himself to abandon all morals and become one of the pirates. In spite of his lowly status among them, he had remained fiercely ambitious. Over time, he had learned to suppress, even conceal this competitive side of his nature but, under pressure, it produced a mean and petty streak which would inevitably reveal its existence by pushing to the surface at some point.

Turning away from the sea at last, Manning was surprised to see Jimmy already gathering kindling, setting it in the shelter of rocks at the edge of the beach and going back to the scrub for larger pieces of wood.

'And how do you plan to light this fire of yours?' Manning asked. Jimmy showed him the tinderbox that Dorothy had placed in his hand. 'Where did you get that?' The look of disdain on Manning's face faded as Jimmy took out the flint and steel, striking them together to produce a spark which dropped in among the dry seaweed and sticks and set them smouldering.

'Dorothy,' Jimmy said, bending close to the ground and blowing gently to produce a tiny flame.

'I'll be damned,' Manning exclaimed.

With the fire blazing, the two young men set about catching crabs in the nearby rock pools. They were small, but the flesh was sweet, with a richness that made them more satisfying, temporarily, than their size would indicate.

When the men had eaten their fill, they piled wood on the fire and settled down to rest in their warm bedrolls.

Manning dreamed of the Swan River Colony, of rolling green hills, with sheep grazing and servants to tend him and his soon-to-be-acquired family. At last, he would be master of his own destiny, no longer at the mercy of eccentric sea captains and unscrupulous pirates. Not since he had first arrived in Sydney Cove, a brash young man full of hopes and plans, had he felt so confident that all would be well. There would be difficult times in the journey ahead, but he would overcome them. He felt that the worst of his misfortunes must surely be behind him.

While James Manning dreamed of a rosy future, Jimmy Newell's thoughts were of the reunion he would soon have with his family at King George Sound. Often in the long winter months, he had wondered what had happened to Mary and Matthew Gill. The ship he was sure Matthew would send for them had never arrived at Middle Island. But many ships had been wrecked in those treacherous waters. The Recherche Archipelago reached out into the Southern Ocean like a chain stretched across the sea-lanes to intercept any ship that dared to venture into the pirates' domain. Too tired to think any more, Jimmy finally fell asleep.

Neither of the young men was aware of the people, clustered on the headland, that watched them curiously, blinking and nodding, before they melted back into the blackness of the night.

In the morning, Manning and Jimmy set off for King George Sound. Keeping the sea on their left, they walked through spinifex and light scrub just above the beach. Their bedrolls were slung on their backs, their hats pulled down to shield their eyes.

The sea was to be both their salvation and their downfall. They could never stray far from it for fear of becoming lost in the vastness of the empty landscape, but its constant proximity brought the glare that quickly burned their skin and the drying winds that parched their throats.

By the end of the first day, their water was almost gone, but they had covered a distance of about thirty miles.

'How long do you reckon it will take?' Manning asked, sucking on the empty shell of a limpet. They had found a sheltered place to camp, but it had no beach and no rock pools. The jagged, black rocks that acted as a windbreak disappeared straight into the sea which drummed against them furiously, sending plumes of salt spray high into the air. The two youths were forced to gather and eat the tiny shellfish that sheltered in the cracks and crevasses of the rocks. Even more fiddly to eat than crabs, they were, nevertheless, full of nutrients. And while the young men now longed for the tammar and mutton-bird stews they had so often complained about on Middle Island, limpets and periwinkles at least took the edge off their hunger.

'The *Mountaineer* did it in about three days, I reckon,' Jimmy said, counting on his fingers. 'Woulda been quicker if Jansen had been payin' more attention to the sailin'.' He grinned at Manning.

'Instead of the women, you mean?'

'And the grog,' Jimmy confirmed.

'Anderson has stolen your sister and my money,' Manning said. 'I intend to make him pay for what he has done. Just see if I don't!' He spat vehemently.

Manning rolled himself into his skins.

While Jimmy gathered driftwood and built up the fire, questions about Manning began to nag at him for the first time.

How would he make Anderson pay? Would Dolly be in danger if he succeeded? Under Anderson's protection, she did seem to be thriving. She had long since ceased to talk of rescue. In fact, away from the distractions of Middle Island, certain things became clearer in Jimmy's mind. He remembered his sister saying she must *visit* King George Sound. Did she not intend to stay?

Hoping to keep his new doubts and the immense wilderness at bay, Jimmy stoked the fire until it blazed.

34

A WEEK PASSED.

In spite of Jimmy's sealskin boots, his feet had begun to blister. After the first few days, he had ceased to feel the pangs of hunger. His shrunken stomach no longer demanded food. He struggled to swallow the native grasses that needed so much chewing that all flavour and moisture went out of them. But he forced them down. They had to keep moving – it was the one thing he knew for certain. At the end of each day they scoured the surrounding rocks and scrub for anything edible. By the next morning, there was nothing left.

Once, they combined forces to catch a sizeable rock cod, Jimmy driving it up under a ledge where James managed to trap it, then flick it out, beating its head against the rock so that the stunned fish could be killed with his knife. They cooked it and ate their fill of the oily flesh, but had no way to dry or preserve what was left. Reluctantly, they abandoned the remains to the gulls. These elegant, silver-grey birds, so different from their much larger, chunkier counterparts on the island, were constant companions as they walked. When they no longer heard the cries of the birds they changed direction, moving closer to the shore which was their only means of navigation.

In the monotonous landscape, it was difficult to get a sense of progress. One set of sandhills looked so much like every other that sometimes Jimmy was convinced that they were travelling in circles, or walking on the spot.

Manning, on the other hand, kept striding ahead with such determination that Jimmy felt drawn along in his wake. There were times when Jimmy lost sight of his companion altogether. This caused such a rush of panic in him that, for a time, he almost ran. But the extra exertion left him totally exhausted. When he caught up with Manning, Jimmy fell at his feet, unable to move. Perhaps, being the smaller of the two, Manning needed less fuel to keep him going. While Jimmy lost weight daily, Manning's wiry body did not seem to change.

'Keep up, will you?' Manning grumbled. 'We'll never get there at this rate.'

Panting and gagging, Jimmy could not speak. His eyes, already sunken in his head, pleaded with Manning as he clutched the tinderbox that he carried inside his shirt.

'Give me that.' Manning reached for the life-preserving box, but Jimmy rolled on top of it, shielding it with his body and kicking out at Manning.

When his breathing steadied, Jimmy said, 'We have to stick together.'

'I know,' Manning conceded moodily. 'Get the fire going.'

The days became warmer, but the nights brought freezing winds, sometimes from the desert, sometimes from the sea, which meant that the shelter they chose in the evening often left them exposed by morning.

Food was scarce, but water was their most pressing problem. When it rained, they raised their faces, mouths open, or cupped their hands to drink from them. Then they ran, stumbling and laughing to the nearest rocks and tried to catch the run-off in their canteens.

Manning recognised some plants, similar to those that grew on Kangaroo Island. He knew which ones were edible and which ones stored water in their root systems to be sucked out later. Once, they saw a slow-moving blue-tongue lizard sunning itself on the warm sand. Jimmy felled it with a well-aimed rock and they set upon it, tearing it apart and eating the white flesh raw.

As the rain fell less and less often, they began to take shelter during the day and walk at night to conserve energy and moisture. On dark nights, their progress was slow. In trying to avoid the steeper sandhills, they often found themselves having to scramble over rocks to escape the incoming tide. Always accompanied by the sound of the sea, they struggled on.

Sometimes, they saw smoke from Aboriginal camp fires further inland. Jimmy was all for setting off towards them.

'They could take us to water,' he said.

'I've no wish to carry a spear in my back!' Manning protested. His experience of the native population around Sydney Cove and of Anderson's dealings with those along the south coast had left him convinced that they were hostile, warlike people. Jimmy tried to persuade him with accounts of the Cockatoo people befriended by Sir Richard Spencer at King George Sound. But Manning would have none of it.

Although Manning spoke like 'gentry' and deplored the manners of the pirates, calling them savages and depraved animals, Jimmy was beginning to see that he could be just as ruthless and inhumane as Anderson. At least with Anderson there was never any pretence. But, having thrown in his lot with his more sophisticated companion, Jimmy was now in a bind. They had to stick together. And Jimmy, by his nature, would always be the one to give in. So they made no attempt to contact the Aboriginal people whose knowledge could have saved them.

Ever more slowly, Manning and Jimmy made their own way towards King George Sound.

35

THE WIND SWUNG TO THE NORTH, BUFFETING THE HUT, BLOWING constantly and uncomfortably from that quarter for almost a week. Rain blew in under the veranda, pooling on the window-sills in spite of the shutters. Cold and dampness seeped into every bone and bedroll in the hollow on Middle Island. Even the mild-mannered William Church was heard to curse as he struggled to keep his firewood dry and stop the smoke from the chimney blowing back into the room.

Everyone was relieved when the sky finally cleared, the air turned crisp, and pale spring sunlight shone on the wet rocks.

Anderson set off at first light, striding towards the beach. His men straggled behind, their breath rising in visible puffs. They grumbled together and clutched their rough garments around them, but they were, nevertheless, pleased to be taking the boat out again. Any sort of activity seemed to improve their tempers, but the sea was the great love of their lives. It freed and cleansed them, restoring their grins and the light, bantering tone to their voices. Quarrelsome individuals on land, in a boat they became a united force.

With the pirates reduced to one boat again, Nurla and Biddi shared the herding work, one going out with the men and the other staying behind to tend the garden, cure the skins and prepare fish and tammar to feed the ravenous sailors, who if they didn't come back that night would be extra hungry when they did return in a day or so. Each night, after those remaining in camp had eaten their fill, the basic stew would be replenished with extra meat and yams, the juices slowly reducing to a deliciously rich gravy that would be soaked up by fresh rolls of damper.

William Church still carefully made his notes, either at the table or, if the sun was shining, in a sheltered corner of the veranda. He filled his notebook twice over – the first time writing from left to right, top to bottom of the page. Then, beginning at the front of the book once more, he turned it sideways and filled it again, writing the words at right angles to, and on top of, the first set. He also developed a new ink substitute, since the berries he had used on the mainland did not grow on Middle Island. After some experimentation, he found that seal blood mixed with wattle sap served his purpose. Although Dorothy could read a little, William's closely written lines were well beyond her skills.

'What does it say?' she would ask. Then Church would read to her details of the seal catch, the tanning process, the food they ate and the stories that were told after dinner.

With both Mary and Jimmy gone, Dorothy found herself confiding in Church more and more. She related stories of her family, of their life in England and their journey to Australia, her own perspective on the wreck of the *Mountaineer* and the traumatic aftermath. As her trust in him deepened, she began to reveal some of the more intimate details of her relationship with Anderson. All of this William Church recorded.

Dorothy continued to visit the women's camp daily. Still shy and often busy, Biddi nevertheless welcomed her, chatting away in broken English and offering a very strong brew of bush-tea. Nurla seemed more reticent, but gradually, a friendship of sorts developed between all three of them.

Dorothy fought new feelings of jealousy when Biddi described how she and Nurla belonged to Anderson, and how this belonging protected them from the attentions of the other sealers.

But when Biddi spoke of her baby, taken from her by a mysterious illness in spite of all that Nurla could do, Dorothy wanted to hug her, such painful memories of her own family were stirred by the words.

Although they were beginning to understand each other, there was a distance between them that could never quite be bridged.

Dorothy's only other companion on the island was Johnno. While his antics were amusing, he often found coherent speech difficult and became tongue-tied in her company. To spare him the embarrassment, Dorothy tended to avoid him and was quite relieved whenever he went out in the boat.

Anderson and his men were often away, sometimes for days on end. Dorothy never knew where they went or how long they would be gone. No matter who else stayed behind, the camp was different when Anderson himself was not there. She missed him.

On her daily walks, Dorothy frequently passed the place where she and Mary had rested beside the well. Wondering where Mary was now, Dorothy felt a twinge of guilt. She should have stayed closer to her sister, in spite of their differences. Life, she had learned, was too precious to be marred by petty quarrels.

She climbed the ridge above the beach and sat looking out across the water to the mainland. Jimmy had been gone nearly three months, Mary four. Because she could not bear to do otherwise, she imagined them both leading normal lives, buying goods at the store and grog at the pub, laughing and chatting with the other settlers, then going home to the cottage above the Sound to sleep in a proper bed. While she had come to love the wild freedom of the island, she needed to visit them, to make contact with her family and put her new life into perspective.

Unlike Dorothy, Church had never tried to communicate directly with Nurla and Biddi. He feared Anderson's wrath, but in another way he feared the women themselves. Although benign, their alien presence was a constant reminder of how his life had changed, of how much he missed his native land and the company of like-minded people. He recognised that the Aboriginal women, too, had been displaced, taken away from their families and homes. But their ability to adapt to their new situation only served to underline his own failure.

'That one sky-spirit?' Biddi asked when Dorothy mentioned William Church's note-taking one day. Dorothy was about to ask what a sky-spirit was, when Johnno appeared. He had moved silently across the patch of bare ground in front of the humpy, swept clean each day by one or other of the women.

'They think he's a h-holy man,' Johnno said. 'They fear the m-m-marks on the page for they ain't never seen n-n-nothin' like it.'

Biddi used her index finger to scribble on her palm. Imitating the act of writing she said, 'Catch him spirit. Make him sit down there, long time.' Nervously she fingered the shells around her neck as if for protection and reassurance. 'No good,' she declared. 'Spirit must go free.'

Dorothy looked at Johnno, but he simply shrugged and walked away, carrying his bush-cut waddy like a musket on his shoulder.

When Dorothy reported this exchange to William Church, later, she expected him to laugh. Instead he frowned.

'Would that I had such powers,' he said. 'For I long to escape from here.'

Dorothy, on the other hand, felt that Middle Island was slowly taking her over, becoming her true home. Food was plentiful, if a trifle monotonous. The hut was basic, but spacious and comfortable. If she could just put her mind at rest about her family, she could declare herself as happy as she had ever been.

Fresh meat and fish were always available, but stores had become desperately low. Anderson's most recent raids on passing ships had produced money, jewellery, clothing – including some new dresses for Dorothy – and other valuable items, but very little food.

Then the day came when there was no more flour for damper.

'Bundle up the skins,' Anderson said. A buzz of anticipation circled among the crew. They were going to the Sound.

36

ON THE MAINLAND, THIN TRAILS OF SMOKE FROM THE ABORIGINAL fires surrounded James Manning and Jimmy Newell, but they had gone beyond noticing or caring. More than a month had passed since Black Jack Anderson had set them ashore. Their bodies were emaciated, their lips cracked and bleeding. Flies crawled constantly into every corner of their eyes and mouths. They suffered them with silent lethargy, having long ago given up any attempt at brushing them away.

All their efforts had become concentrated on putting one foot in front of the other. Walking at night had become more trouble than it was worth. Each time they stumbled and fell in the darkness it was more difficult to rise. The effort of picking themselves up was almost too much. They made more progress by sleeping at night and walking in the cooler mornings and evenings. Not that there was much evidence of progress. With so few landmarks along the endless coastline it was only the sea, roaring, beating, breathing beside them and the fact that their bodies were constantly tired that gave them any sensation of movement.

As the weeks passed, they barely spoke to each other, saving their breath and energy for walking. Sometimes, Jimmy would fall behind, stumbling, forcing his large, gaunt frame upright, falling again until he cried out for Manning not to leave him. Reluctant to break the plodding rhythm of his own steps, Manning would turn his head, but continue on for some distance. Never so far as to lose sight of Jimmy, though.

For all his contempt for the faithful Jimmy, James Manning knew that their only hope of survival now was to stick together. Besides, Jimmy carried the tinderbox and steadfastly refused to give it up, saying it was his – a gift from Dorothy. He guarded it so jealously that Manning decided that the boy had rarely been given gifts or even shown much kindness in his life. With his simple nature, his shallow forehead and his tongue always seeming too big for his mouth, even before it became swollen with thirst, Manning imagined the younger boy reviled by his peers, the butt of jokes in his village long before he arrived on Middle Island.

They walked until their steps were barely more than a shuffle. What clothes they had left hung off them in ragged strips. They had abandoned their bedrolls long ago and now slept where they fell with little attempt at finding shelter.

During the colder nights, when the wind seemed to cut through their flesh and reside in their bones, they burrowed into the sand, leaving hollow depressions that a group of Aborigines would find the next day.

Every morning, they coaxed their stiff limbs into action, their empty bellies forcing them on.

Towards the end of the second month, with no idea how far they had come or how much further they had to go, the two young men stumbled upon a patch of wet ground. Water was seeping out of the hillside. They dug frantically with their bare hands, oblivious to the tearing of skin and nails, and uncovered a spring of fresh water. They drank and washed. Their parched throats cracked and cackled with laughter. They were so unaccustomed to the sound of their own voices that they stared at each other in amazement. The sun was high, but the cold wind chapped their wet skin. They lay down to rest in a shallow cave near by and fell into the deep sleep of exhaustion.

37

THERE HAD BEEN ONE NIGHT WHEN JOHNNO, NEVER VERY STEADY on his feet, stumbled while loading his plate and accidentally spilled hot stew on Isaac's boots. Winterbourne immediately delivered a reflex blow, lashing out at Johnno with the knife. The other men found the situation either outrageous or funny, according to their allegiances. Perhaps at that moment something snapped in his clouded brain, but the usually good-natured Johnno, bleeding freely from the gash across his forearm, recovered his balance, raised his plate in both hands and brought it down hard on Winterbourne's head. Bits of meat and gravy lodged in Winterbourne's hair and beard, causing peels of laughter of a different sort. But Dorothy, who had been standing next to the pot, was alarmed by the murderous look in Winterbourne's eyes. She backed away and sought the protection of the wall.

Anderson, who had been outside, came back to find the hut in chaos. Striding in, he grabbed Winterbourne's upraised arm just as he was about to deliver a second, more deadly, blow to Johnno.

Winterbourne struggled to free himself from the big man's

grasp. Anderson tightened his grip and jerked the knife from Winterbourne's hand. The smaller man bent to retrieve his weapon, but Anderson covered it with his booted foot. With one tilt of his head, Anderson sent Johnno out to find Nurla and get his wound treated. Only when Johnno was well away did he move his foot to uncover the knife. Scowling darkly, Winterbourne picked it up and placed it in the sheath that hung from his belt.

Conversations in the room were taken up again and more rum, the apparent cure for all disturbances, was passed around. Dorothy resumed the unfinished task of stacking plates and partly overheard William saying something to Gimble. She caught Winterbourne's name as Gimble shoved his blunt fingers up under his headscarf to scratch at his scalp.

'He's a sly dog, to be sure,' the Irishman said. 'But Anderson has his measure.' Having reassured himself of this, Gimble got up from the table and refilled his mug.

'Winterbourne is trouble,' Dorothy said later when she and Anderson had settled into bed.

'Aye, he has a chip on his shoulder the size of a yardarm,' Anderson agreed.

'Surely Nimble Gimble would make a better first mate. He is ten times more trustworthy,' Dorothy suggested. Anderson did not respond immediately, but lay with his hands behind his head as he often did when he was thinking.

'Gimble,' he said at last, 'he be like your Jimmy. A good sailor and a brave man. But, like your Jimmy, he ain't no leader. Winterbourne's a dangerous enemy. Better he be believin' I'm his friend.'

It soon became clear that, although Anderson had decided to go to King George Sound, he was not planning to take Dorothy with him.

'It ain't the *Mountaineer* we be sailin' in, woman,' he reminded her when she found out she was being left behind. 'Agin the Roarin' Forties we won't have no easy run.'

'But I *must* go,' Dorothy pleaded, clamping both hands to her chest as if to hold the panic in.

'Women bring bad luck aboard,' Anderson said gruffly.

'What about Biddi and Nurla?' Dorothy spluttered. Her initial panic turned to outrage.

'That's different,' Anderson said, glaring at her. But she glared back, refusing to look away. 'They work,' he said, softening a little.

'I can be useful.' She lifted her chin, pride making her body stiff and angular.

'You can at that.' Anderson laughed and reached out one arm towards her. Dorothy relaxed and allowed herself to be drawn in to his embrace. She felt her bristling anger soften and smooth out as he held her close and gently ran his hand beneath the thick rope of hair that had fallen across her breast, lifting and brushing it back so that her auburn locks hung, once again, behind her shoulder. She placed her own hand over his. Was this the iron fist that struck fear into so many men?

The crew set about their preparations with a will. There were repairs to be carried out on the Beetle. Skins to be tied in bundles. Vegetables and dried fish to be packed into barrels. The usual grumblings when there was work to be done on shore were replaced with jokes and ribald laughter. A trip to the Sound would mean plenty of grog and women. It would also be a rare chance to socialise outside of their own small group.

But for Dorothy, the work seemed frustratingly slow and she wondered if Anderson had not deliberately set the men unnecessary tasks to put off their departure, knowing now that she was determined to go with him.

She tried to be patient, but found herself running along the beaches where she usually walked and shouting into the wind at the top of Flinders Peak. This went some way towards releasing the tensions in her body, but it did nothing to improve her temper.

With the Beetle finally repaired, Dorothy was sure they would set off the next day. She was furious when Anderson decided on one last sealing trip to supplement provisions for the journey.

'Must you go?' she pleaded, trying to hide her frustration.

'I'll be back afore you know it,' he promised.

The boat returned two days later and the men carried their catch up from the beach. Stacking the fresh carcasses on the edge of the salt lake, they set about removing the skins, spreading them out to dry, separating the meat and leaving the blubber for Nurla and Biddi to boil down for oil.

Since Bathurst had gone, Anderson had trusted no one else to oversee the stowing of the gear and securing of the Beetle. Dorothy ran down to the beach to meet him, but stopped short of making contact. She stood on the flat rock, watching.

Preoccupied as he was with stowing the sail and stretching the oiled canvas cover over the hull, she could not be sure that he had seen her. When he was satisfied that his task was complete, he looked up, acknowledging her presence for the first time.

'Have you spoken to Gimble?' he asked, his face a mask that gave nothing away.

'No, why?'

'He has . . .' Anderson hesitated, '. . . summit to tell.'

Dorothy ran to find Nimble Gimble.

He was not in the clearing. The other men looked up briefly at her agitated face, but resumed the cleaning and sharpening of their knives without comment. There were voices coming from the direction of the lake. She hurried along the swampy path.

'Arr, Miss Newell.' Gimble saw her coming and waited. Dorothy stepped aside, allowing Ernest Hill to pass before she and Gimble made their way to higher, dryer ground where Gimble related to Dorothy what he had heard.

The sealing party had encountered another boat fishing in the area. Both groups had landed on a nearby island and, after exchanging news and gossip, shared a meal before going their separate ways, Anderson's men carefully avoiding giving any hint of the whereabouts of their base. Although it was common knowledge by then that the pirates lived somewhere in the archipelago, with 105 islands to choose from, their exact location was not widely known. Gimble had been part of a conversation with a man from the other group who repeated a rumour he had heard. Two white men, so he said, had been carried in to Albany by the local Aborigines and deposited with the Government Resident.

'Alive?' Dorothy stared at Gimble. When he didn't reply immediately, she grabbed his arm in her eagerness. 'Please.'

Surprised by the physical contact, Gimble stiffened, but took pity on her desperation.

'I . . . don't rightly know,' he said. It was, in any case, just a rumour, he insisted. His informant was 'after drinkin' an awful lot of rum.' And was not the most reliable of men. 'Economical with the truth, ya might say.'

Dorothy could not get any more information from him, and eventually had to accept that Gimble himself knew nothing more. She tried to hide her disappointment. But the need to know what had happened to Jimmy, Mary, her mother, little William and the others had become urgent. But since none of them could read and write, and no postal service was ever likely to extend to Middle Island, she had only one way of finding out how they were faring and of letting them know that she was alive and well.

'Do you miss *your* family, Mr Church?' Dorothy asked, slumping down beside him as he dipped a newly sharpened quill into his inky concoction. William Church paused, his pen suspended while the precious liquid dripped back into the rough clay pot.

'My family, my books, picnics on green grass . . .' He gazed out at the dirt clearing, surrounded by the pale trunks of paperbark trees with their bark hanging in ragged, untidy strips. Beyond that, the low grey scrub stretched away in monotonous profusion.

'We *will* go to the Sound,' Dorothy assured him, in a voice she had often used with her younger siblings.

'I am afraid that any future I might have lies in the opposite direction,' William Church said flatly.

'But there will be ships at the Sound to take you to Hobart Town,' Dorothy said, wanting him to share her enthusiasm. He shrugged his shoulders in a gesture of defeat.

'I have given up caring what happens to me,' he said. 'But my notes must be preserved so that justice can be done.' His back straightened and his body was suddenly charged with surprising strength. 'In the eyes of the law, all these men will be lumped together and found equally guilty. But some are here by misadventure and have sought to make the best of their lot – as we do.'

His eyes shone feverishly and Dorothy grew concerned that he might be unwell.

'I believe that Anderson is not entirely bad,' Church continued, 'but a man forced by circumstances of birth and experience to fight for his own survival. And Gimble. He has told me much that has surprised and enlightened me. Both are blaggards, of course, but who are we to judge the colour of a man's soul? I am making a copy of my notes. If I die here, they will be discovered by future visitors to this island. Perhaps too late to be of use to the present generation. But one can only hope that history will be informed and the true stories of these men revealed.'

'Ya must not worry so, Mr Church. We are safer now than we ever were with Captain Jansen.'

'And if there is a price on Anderson's head?' Church asked. But Dorothy ignored his fears. She was determined not to let anything spoil her excitement. Anderson had managed, on previous visits, to escape unscathed. In spite of the many complaints against him, he had never been formally charged. Lack of evidence was usually given as the reason, but Dorothy wondered if the Albany traders wouldn't rather have him free to go about his sealing business than locked up in the town at their expense. The arrest of Anderson would mean that a very lucrative part of their trade would be lost. There were other sealers, of course, but Anderson and his crew were by far the most successful. The pelts they brought, or sent via other trading ships, were always in good condition, highly prized by the London buyers who bought them for up to twelve times what the sealers were paid.

No, William Church was overly cautious, she decided.

38

IN ALBANY, SIR RICHARD SPENCER OPENED HIS DOOR IN RESPONSE TO a knock. Shocked by the scene before him, he drew in a sharp breath.

'Black Anderson. Black Anderson.' The words emanated faintly from what appeared to be a living skeleton. The magistrate leaned closer. The stench of rotting flesh drove him back, but the bloodshot eyes, crusted and rimmed with dirt, had latched on to his own and held fast with wild determination. The remnants of clothing hung like filthy rags around the man's neck and waist. Burnt by the sun, covered in sores and too weak to walk, he lay like a broken scarecrow in the arms of one of the local Aboriginal men.

Spencer knew these Aborigines. They belonged to the group known as Cockatoo people and had accepted his gifts of flour, sugar and cloth from time to time. He was unable to speak more than a few words of their language, nor they his, but he motioned them to set their burden down on the veranda of the Government Cottage. It was only then that he saw the second white man. Carried piggyback style, limbs dangling loose, the head of long, matted hair lolling on the shoulder of his rescuer, this one appeared to be already dead.

When both bodies had been lowered to the boards, Sir Richard offered his right hand in thanks to the leader of the group. The man shook it, European fashion. Then the whole group turned and disappeared back into the bush.

Grass-filled mattresses, prepared by Spencer's servants, were placed on the floor in the main room of the cottage. More logs were added to the open fire in the grate. Water was brought in a shallow bowl and both men were bathed. Thin soup, warmed and carried from the separate building that housed the kitchen, was carefully spooned in between the men's cracked lips. The 'dead' man opened his eyes, but it would be several days before either of them was capable of revealing who they were or where they had come from.

A blustery south wind blew straight from the Antarctic, whipping the Southern Ocean into a frenzy of white-capped waves that broke on the shores of the Sound and sent cold sprays of water up into the streets of the tiny settlement of Albany. Inside the Government Cottage, however, it was warm and dry.

At about midday on the tenth of August 1835, Sir Richard Spencer came striding into the room where the two men lay on their temporary beds.

'Ah,' he said, looking down at them, 'I see that your health has improved.'

'I'm much obliged to you, sir.' James Manning spoke first, as he would continue to do over the next few weeks. 'You are most kind . . . to take us in.' Although he still struggled to speak above a whisper, it was clear that he was articulate and well educated. His companion had not spoken, but the servants reported that he had managed to swallow some of the solid food that was placed in his mouth.

'Your name is James, I believe.' Although he addressed Manning, both men nodded. Sir Richard looked surprised, but then it was, after all, a common name. 'Perhaps you could tell me where you have come from?' In spite of his scarred face and reputation for gruff impatience, the Resident spoke gently. James Manning struggled to get up. 'No, please, you must rest.' Manning sank gratefully back onto the pillow. 'We will prepare an official declaration when you are fully recovered. For now, an informal interview will suffice.'

'I had booked a passage to the Swan River Colony on the schooner *Defiance* . . .' James Manning began. Sir Richard Spencer took out his notebook and the young man told his tale of adventure and misadventure.

Anchored in the harbour at Botany Bay, the *Defiance* had looked to be a fine ship. A solid schooner of 25 tons with a cargo of provisions for trading with the sealers, she rode the waves with ease and grace. There were rumours that her commander, Mr George Merredith, was eccentric and unstable but, by all accounts, an excellent seaman.

They sailed down the east coast in good weather, but rounding Cape Howe they were dogged by storms, high winds and huge swells. During the night, their main mast broke and the ship ran aground on Cape Howe Island.

At this point in the narrative, Sir Richard paused and

looked up from his notebook. He and his family, with all their household goods, their animals and nine of their best servants, had battled the same high seas. He offered up silent thanks that they had arrived safely on the shores of Australia and had not suffered a similar fate to this young man. Then he bent again to the task of recording James Manning's story.

39

NEWS OF THE TWO WHITE MEN SPREAD RAPIDLY THROUGH THE TOWN of Albany. Who were they? Where had they come from? No one arrived in the tiny harbour town except by sea. It was as if these two emaciated creatures had dropped from the sky.

The Aborigines had carried them in to the town, that much was certain. Some said from 10 miles out, some said 100 miles. The nearest civilisation, at the Swan River Colony, was 300 miles to the north. It was inconceivable that they had walked from there. But where was their ship? And if it was wrecked somewhere along the coast, what had happened to their companions? It did not occur to the people of Albany that these two young men had come overland from the desolate, unexplored east – the other side.

James Newell Senior was summoned to the Resident's cottage. At first, he did not recognise his son. There was no sign of the strong, well-built fifteen-year-old lad who had left on the *Mountaineer* six months before. In his place was this ancient-looking creature with bones almost protruding through flaky grey skin. Covered in sores, his blackened tongue visible between cracked and swollen lips that he was unable to close, the young man still lay close to death. Only his eyes, although haunted and unfocused, remained his own.

When Mary and Matthew Gill had returned with Jansen in the *Mountaineer*'s whaleboat the previous month the Newells had expected that Matthew would double the family income by getting a job, as James Newell Senior had, at the now flourishing Strawberry Hill Farm.

But Matthew had other plans. Mary had declared she would never undertake another sea voyage. Within a week of Jimmy and Manning's arrival in Albany, however, she and Matthew left Albany to work their passage on a schooner going to Sydney Cove. All ideas of making a quick fortune had been lost with the *Mountaineer*. But Matthew was still ambitious. He had decided that the larger colony in New South Wales offered more possibilities, even if the best land had already been taken. And, as his wife, Mary had no choice but to go with him.

With the departure of Matthew and Mary, things had become increasingly desperate for what was left of the Newell family. James Newell's meagre wages did not go far with two adults and four growing children to feed. His wife's health continued to deteriorate, mainly due to her excessive drinking, and she suffered from the shame she felt at having to ask for handouts from people in the town. The family's debts mounted. They owed money everywhere.

'Oh, that it should come to this,' Hannah wailed to her husband. 'We came here to make something of our lives, to be landowners and no longer servants. But we are no better off than those wretched Aborigines.' She threw herself down on the bed and refused to get up for two days.

When the news came that those same Aborigines had carried her son back from the brink of certain death Hannah was grateful, in a detached sort of way, but soon lapsed again into the blessed oblivion produced by alcohol. The damage had been done.

Jimmy Newell did not immediately return to the tumble-down and overcrowded house occupied by his family at King George Sound. He and James Manning were slowly nursed back to health in the Government cottage where Sir Richard Spencer's servants fed, washed and administered ointments and potions to the ravaged bodies of the two young men.

It was more than a month before Jimmy was able to take some tentative steps. Having walked for so long in a semi-conscious state, it was as if his mind could no longer persuade his body to perform that painful and traumatic action. When he was finally helped from his makeshift bed, he could not even stand. His only method of getting about unaided was to crawl like a baby until gradually, with regular food and exercise, his muscles began to respond. But he remained confused and disoriented, plagued by nightmares and easy prey to the manipulation of Manning, who had recovered much more quickly. Within a week, James Manning was demanding from his bed that charges be brought against Black Jack Anderson.

Although Manning was convinced that the big American was the main culprit, he also brought charges against Isaac Winterbourne, as Anderson's accomplice.

Sir Richard took formal statements from both young men as soon as they were able to talk at length. The government agent was keen for the proper processes of the law to be carried out in the town of Albany. He had already vastly improved its economic fortunes and was working hard to attract more settlers. He was eager to dispel any perception that it was still a rough frontier settlement.

40

ON MIDDLE ISLAND THERE WAS A SENSE OF EXCITEMENT. DOROTHY was lifted into the bow of the whaleboat. The strong arms of Anderson scooped her up as if there was no more weight to her than a bedroll. William Church, his precious satchel bulging with rolls of paperbark carefully wrapped in oiled cloth, stepped in behind her. Winterbourne and Hill secured the provisions and raised the sail before taking up their positions at the oars. With Anderson standing in the stern, Gimble and Mead pushed the Beetle out into deeper water and leapt aboard.

After helping to load the piles of skins, Biddi, Nurla and Johnno stood back, watching from the beach. They would stay and keep the lizards and tammars from taking over the hut while the others were away.

The sea sparkled, calm and inviting, as they set off with the rising sun at their backs painting the clouds overhead with gold and pink and red. They were on their way at last. Dorothy would see her family, hold little William, exchange gossip with Mary. Although she had found a growing contentment on the island, she had missed her family.

And she wondered how Jimmy and Manning had fared. Long ago, she had convinced herself that there was nothing she could have done to prevent Jimmy from leaving. There was no point in dwelling on the events leading up to their departure. Anderson assured her that he had no knowledge of James Manning's forty-six pounds and she believed him. To Dorothy, it was a lot of money. But given his own undisputed wealth, why would Anderson steal from Manning?

Thoughts raced through her mind as Dorothy saw Middle Island become a dot on the horizon behind them. In spite of her excitement, she was surprised at how much like leaving home it felt. She knew she was, in many ways, a different person now. In one of the most difficult and dangerous environments on earth she had managed to carve out a place for herself, a place where she had control of her own life and the respect of others.

Dorothy was in high spirits as they made their way past the numerous islands of the archipelago. She pictured the sheltered waters of the Sound, the wooden jetty and the climb up the slope to the family cottage. It would be great to walk on a street again, call to the neighbours, go to a shop.

She thought of her father, her mother and all the children. Anderson was an expert sailor. The best in the Southern Ocean. Everyone said so. And she knew that she could trust him with her life. But she wondered what her family would think of him. He had made the sea his constant companion. Homes and families ashore were for other men.

In an earlier bid to deter Dorothy from coming, Anderson

had been deliberately vague about how long the journey to King George Sound would take. All he would say was that they would shelter on the islands or in the mainland bays at night and sail during the daylight hours, just as the survivors had done in those terrible days after the *Mountaineer* was wrecked. But to Dorothy, this journey felt so different. With the sun shining, and the wind blowing from the east, filling their sail so that they sliced through the water with ease, she refused to believe that anything could go wrong.

41

BY THE TIME BLACK JACK ANDERSON BEACHED HIS WHALEBOAT IN King George Sound on that September day in 1835, it had become a very different place from the one Dorothy Newell had left behind six months before.

'Netty!' Dorothy called, and waved excitedly to her sister, who was already hurrying towards the beach as fast as the weight of the two-year-old boy bouncing on her hip would allow. There were many more houses than there had been in the town, and most of them were built overlooking the harbour. News of any new arrival spread quickly.

'Dolly, is it really you?' The young women embraced each other while William squirmed down onto the sand and began throwing fistfuls of it in the air, much more interested in his own excavations than in this long-forgotten sister. Dorothy lifted him up to her eye level, holding him under the arms and laughing at the unexpected size of him.

'It is really me, Netty, but who is this? William! Where are ya baby curls?' The child regarded her curiously, kicking his dangling legs and wriggling so much that she set him down on his feet again and turned back to her sister. 'Now tell me, is Mary here? And Jimmy? Are they well?'

With the boat secured, Anderson stood on the beach and watched Dorothy walk away, one arm around her sister's waist, the other holding the hand of the toddler.

William Church, with his hat jammed on his head and his battered satchel clutched tightly, was already making his way towards the cluster of buildings that now made up the main street.

The other men hovered, waiting for instructions before unloading the precious skins. The unwritten law, strictly adhered to by the pirates, that they would all share equally in any money or goods acquired by the group, meant that everyone must be present when important transactions were carried out.

'Get to work then,' Anderson barked, finally turning away from the retreating backs of the three Newells.

Dorothy and Netty chatted constantly, occasionally glancing down at William and slowing their pace as he struggled, gasping and coughing, to keep up. Although Netty had described the situation to her, Dorothy was still shocked when they arrived at the house. It looked so neglected. There were gaps in the wattle-and-daub walls where chunks of daub had fallen off and not been replaced. The roof was sagging under the weight of its heavy thatch and the garden, which should have been the lifeblood of the household, was overgrown with weeds and native grasses. It seemed that Jimmy had not recovered fully from his ordeal and no one else had the time or energy to carry out even the most basic repairs.

'Oh, Netty,' Dorothy sighed.

'I'm so glad you're back.' Her sister embraced her again, clinging to her so tightly that Dorothy could hardly breathe.

Hannah Newell spent most of the time in an alcoholic haze, occasionally emerging to complain about the state of the place in general and her own situation in particular. Her husband did what he could. Now that Sir Richard Spencer had established Strawberry Hill Farm and encouraged the other settlers to run their sheep on more suitable pastures, labourers were in demand. But James Newell often had to travel twenty miles from the settlement, since the land closer in was useless for crops and grazing. If he couldn't get a lift in a wagon taking stores or with another landowner making a visit, he walked. But that often meant that he was away from home for as long as the job took to complete. He returned with money. But it was quickly spent on grog to celebrate his return and to keep Hannah happy.

Within a day or so of her arrival, Dorothy had organised the older children to weed the garden, plant new seeds that she procured from Sir Richard Spencer's nursery and tidy up the house. She could not help thinking of the sturdy, well-built hut, the constantly tended garden and the bountiful supplies of meat, oil for heating and skins to wear, all free of charge on Middle Island.

On the third day, she sought out Anderson in the pub. She had come to ask him for money to put flour, tea and sugar in her family's larder.

'Is your business completed?' Dorothy asked once she and

Anderson had escaped from the noise and the stifling atmosphere of the pub and were walking together along the cliff above the beach. Tongues would wag among the gossips in the town, but Dorothy refused to care.

'We sold our skins,' Anderson said.

'Has Manning asked for a share?' Dorothy asked.

'The snivelling bilge-rat!' A sharp burst of anger shook Anderson, but was quickly replaced by an uncharacteristic air of resignation. 'We ain't gonna talk about it.' He reached out his hand and Dorothy placed her own in it.

The two figures walked along the cliff, finally making their way down a sandy slope to a sheltered cove – the same cove where Anderson had rested nine years before. Much had changed in his life, but here the rocks, the sea, the sand, even the noisy gulls, were reassuringly the same. Sun and wind, storms and tides, had all visited his cave. Their battering had made little impact. The rough, weathered exterior still concealed a place of warmth and safety at its heart.

It was late, past midnight, when Dorothy returned to the family cottage above the harbour.

42

LATE IN THE MORNING, NETTY CAME BURSTING IN TO THE NEWELL cottage. Her face was red from running and her bonnet, held only by its ribbons, hung at the back of her neck. Stores spilled from the shopping basket as she dropped it to the floor.

'Anderson has been arrested!'

'No!' Dorothy gasped. 'Tell me it's not true! It's cruel of ya to joke about this, Netty.' Dorothy did not know whether to laugh or cry. She had not believed for a moment that the rumoured charges would actually be laid.

'I'm not joking, Dolly. His boat is impounded and Anderson himself taken to the guardhouse in chains!' Netty tried to catch her breath. 'He must appear in court on Monday! And Winterbourne, too.'

'Winterbourne?' Dorothy registered the name, but had no interest in anyone but Anderson. 'Why now?'

'James Manning,' Netty said, flinging herself down on the nearest chair, her chest still heaving from her exertions.

'Manning!' Dorothy exclaimed. 'Surely no one believes him!'

'Sir Richard Spencer obviously does,' Netty continued. 'He is asking about witnesses.'

'What witnesses?' Dorothy pictured the clearing on Middle Island and longed for the peace and freedom of her uncomplicated life there.

'I heard your name spoken. And that of William Church,' Netty told her. 'Have the soldiers been yet?'

'Don't be ridiculous, Netty.' Dorothy's voice crackled with indignation. 'I'll be givin' them a piece of my mind if they do come! The hide of James Manning, after all that Anderson has done for him! I will never understand how Jimmy can call that little snake in the grass a friend.'

Dorothy had listened to the tales of privation, exhaustion and near death that the two youths had suffered. But that was hardly Anderson's fault. Manning had demanded to be put ashore. She had heard him with her own ears. And as for Anderson stealing his money, she was convinced that the small-minded Isaac Winterbourne had taken it to make up the percieved shortfall in his own purse. She had begun to hate, as well as mistrust, the little Englishman. It was bad enough on Middle Island, but in Albany his bitter features seemed to pop up everywhere so that she wondered if he wasn't following her. At one point she had steeled herself to confront him, only to find, when she turned around, that he had vanished.

'Gimble – and the others. They will speak for Anderson,' Dorothy insisted.

'They may look to savin' their own necks, Dolly,' Netty warned.

The trial was held in the recently erected guardhouse between the military and civilian prisons, within easy reach of the sea. The gales of the first week in September had abated and the morning dawned clear and still as the townspeople gathered in the courtyard outside the building. There was little other entertainment available to them and, they were curious about this almost legendary pirate. With a reputation for giving no quarter and expecting none in return, Black Jack Anderson had always avoided capture in the past by disappearing into the Southern Ocean with the speed of a westerly breeze. And yet here he was, defiantly standing his ground while others of his crew fled into the bush. It was almost as if the big man welcomed this delay to his departure.

At nine in the morning, the doors were opened. The waiting people filed in, filling the small, bare room where a dozen mismatched chairs had been arranged in front of a long wooden table. Behind the table three much more ornate and official-looking chairs had been placed.

Voices were hushed at first as the people spoke to each other in the unfamiliar setting. But they became louder as opinions, already divided, were expressed more forcefully and discussions threatened to turn into arguments.

Eventually, Sir Richard Spencer entered. Captain Alex Cheyne and Mr Peter Belches, both justices of the peace, followed. They were dressed in their best suits, the high-winged collars of their starched shirts firmly fastened with black ties. Sir Richard Spencer wore the full uniform of a captain in the Royal Navy, but even his gold braid and ramrod straight back could not disguise the horrific injuries he had suffered while serving in the Napoleonic Wars. It was said that, although his skull was fractured by a glancing blow from a cannon ball, he had refused to be taken below. Bleeding profusely and propping his mangled head on the crossbeam, he had drawn his sword and engaged the enemy as they boarded his ship, only succumbing when a blow from an enemy sword had almost cut his face in half. A white ridge of scar tissue ran from left to right across his forehead and between his eyes, ending a little below the tip of his ear. Although he was never completely free of pain, the same determination that had enabled him to survive the wars he now applied to the tasks of government resident and magistrate in this tiny outpost of the British Empire.

He walked around the table and pulled out the middle chair of the three. Its solid legs scraped on the floor, making the only sound in the now hushed room. Captain Cheyne and Mr Belches stood on either side of Sir Richard, waiting until the magistrate was seated. Then Captain Cheyne ordered the prisoners brought in from their cells.

All heads turned towards the door and a new murmur of voices swirled around the room as Anderson and Winterbourne, their hands manacled in front of them, were escorted in by soldiers on either side.

There could not have been two more opposite-looking men. Winterbourne, with his sallow skin, his stiff hair and long beard, his too-large coat hanging off narrow, slightly stooped shoulders. And the giant Anderson, his smooth, almost hairless black skin taut and shining as he stood proudly in the dock, head held high, looking like some exotic Zulu chieftain in his long sealskin cloak.

43

'JOHN WILLIAM ANDERSON, YOU ARE CHARGED THAT, ON THE twenty-third day of June last, you did steal from Mr James Manning the sum of forty-six pounds, fifteen shillings, and did threaten to shoot him with your pistol – how do you plead?'

Anderson neither moved nor spoke. His gaze was fixed on one of the windows through which an expanse of sea and the distant misty hills of Flinders Peninsula could be seen. But his jaw was clenched, his thick lips pulled tight.

'Answer the question or you will be further charged with contempt of this court!' Captain Cheyne demanded.

'Not guilty,' Anderson grunted, turning to glare over the heads of the crowd.

'Not guilty, *Your Honour*!' Cheyne insisted.

With an impatient wave of his hand, Sir Richard pressed on. 'I have before me the signed declarations of Mr James Manning and Mr James Newell. However, since there appear to be certain discrepancies in the accounts of the incident in question, the court requires some clarification of these events. The case for the prosecution will now be heard.'

James Manning took the stand. Placing his hand on the leather-bound Bible, he was sworn in by Mr Belches.

After a brief glance at his accuser, Anderson again focused his attention on a point somewhere behind and above the crowd.

Dorothy pushed forward through the press of people in the room. Anderson noticed her movement and their eyes met briefly. Dorothy feared for him, but smiled inwardly at his proud bearing, his refusal to be intimidated by these dauntingly formal proceedings. She found herself taking courage from his example and became determined to see justice done for this man she had come to know so intimately. She did not use the word 'love', even to herself. It seemed too great a burden to load onto a relationship begun out of necessity. And yet, she felt that they did belong to each other. She was his – and he was hers, by virtue of their shared need and the trust that had grown between them.

'Am I correct in my understanding that this sum of money was sewn into the lining of a canvas bag, Mr Manning?' Sir Richard Spencer's voice cut across Dorothy's thoughts.

'Yes, Your Honour.' James Manning managed to turn the nod that accompanied his words into an obsequious bowing of his head.

'And this canvas bag was similar to one allegedly saved from the wreck of the *Mountaineer* by Captain Evanson Jansen, was it not?'

'Similar, sir, but not the same.'

'How was it different?'

James Manning explained at great length how the bag that belonged to him had been repaired with twine made from the sinews of tammar tails and that, at the time of the robbery, only Anderson had access to such twine. Manning himself, having used all his own supply, had asked around the group whether anyone else had any. Since all the others on Middle Island said they had only string made from reeds and vines, the bag must have been opened and resewn by Anderson.

'Your own supply of twine had been exhausted, you say. Were you in the habit of doing a lot of sewing, Mr Manning?'

Manning's haughty self-assurance began to slip as he tried to foresee where the questions were leading.

'My jacket had suffered from hard wear and was in need of repair, Your Honour,' he said.

'Ah, yes. The same jacket that you previously claimed had forty-six pounds and fifteen shillings sewn into the lining.'

James Manning lowered his eyes and shifted his feet before explaining that he had decided to move the money.

On either side of Sir Richard Spencer, Cheyne and Belches alternately dipped their pens in the central ink jar and wrote in their notebooks.

'And it was you, yourself, who gave this canvas bag to Mr Anderson?'

'For safekeeping, yes.'

'Knowing that it would be kept in a storeroom without a door.'

A low murmur of sound rippled through the courtroom. James Manning's eyes skimmed the crowd, perhaps looking for some indication of support. Sir Richard shuffled the sheaf of papers in front of him and addressed the witness again.

'In his declaration, Mr Newell has said that Mr Anderson threatened you with a pistol and when you pushed the barrel aside, both he and Mr Winterbourne drew their sealing knives. To push aside a pistol, wielded by such a man as Mr Anderson, seems to me a very courageous act on your part, and yet you make no mention of it in your own declaration.'

'I was not myself, sir.'

'You were not yourself at the time of the incident, or at the time of the declaration?'

'I am recently recovered from a life-threatening ordeal, as Your Honour is well aware.' Unsettled now, Manning's voice began to rise with anxiety.

'I merely seek clarification for the benefit of the court,' Sir Richard said calmly. 'Perhaps a short adjournment will assist the cause of justice in this case.'

People turned their attentions away from Manning to focus on their neighbours. In the cramped conditions, any opportunity to stretch their limbs and move their feet was a welcome relief.

44

ANDERSON AND WINTERBOURNE WERE TAKEN BACK TO THE CELLS, but everyone else, including Sir Richard and his two assistants, made their way to the pub, where opinions were freely exchanged and the publican's slate was put to good use.

When the court reconvened, Jimmy Newell took the stand. Also wearing a donated duck frock, he surveyed the courtroom with a slightly dazed expression. His eyes met but slid away from those of his sister Dorothy who had managed to secure one of the public chairs after the break.

'Mr Newell,' Sir Richard began, 'in your statement, made to me on the tenth day of August, you declare that you saw the defendants, John Anderson and Isaac Winterbourne, counting Mr Manning's money.'

There was a long pause in which everyone in the room inclined towards Jimmy Newell, waiting for his response. Finally, Sir Richard repeated the question. Some of the townspeople had found the magistrate short tempered, autocratic, even arrogant, in his dealings with them, but on this occasion he showed none of these traits. His voice was calm, his manner accommodating.

When Jimmy Newell finally nodded his head, Sir Richard asked him, 'How did you know that this particular collection of coins belonged to Mr Manning? Mr Anderson was often in possession of large sums of money, was he not?'

'It was James's money, Your Honour. I knowed it as soon as I saw Black Jack with it in his hands.'

'So it was Mr Anderson and not Mr Winterbourne who was counting the money?'

'No, sir . . . I mean yes, sir.' Obviously confused, Jimmy looked at Manning, whose head was shaking slightly. 'They was both countin' it.'

Sir Richard Spencer tilted his head to study Jimmy Newell with his one good eye. He seemed to ponder the wisdom of questioning the young man further, then said, 'Take your time, Mr Newell. Think carefully about what you saw . . .'

The afternoon wore on. Jimmy Newell's answers were slow and laborious. The heat in the courtroom intensified and the crowd became restless. Dorothy was particularly restless, shifting impatiently in her seat as her brother described how James Manning had shown him a canvas bag, claiming there was a lot of money inside.

'Did you see this money?' Sir Richard asked.

'Umm . . . I don't remember seein' it . . . no. But I heard it rattlin' about.'

This was too much for Dorothy. She leapt to her feet.

'Your Honour,' she declared. 'It is clear that my brother is confused and is still not fully recovered from the journey that almost claimed his life so recently. His memory of events on Middle Island is unreliable to say the least! Any one of a dozen people could have taken James Manning's money – if indeed it was money that Jimmy heard rattling in that bag! In any case I know for a fact that, because he was determined to make the journey to Perth, Mr Anderson offered James Manning fifteen pounds, as a gift. This generosity was immediately and most ungraciously thrown back in Mr Anderson's face!'

Captain Cheyne began to rise to his feet and Sir Richard Spencer looked somewhat surprised by this outburst. Again, he moved his head to improve the line of sight of his good eye, while whispered remarks among the crowd grew louder. But Dorothy faced the courtroom squarely. Her voice was steady now, her body firmly under control. Sir Richard allowed her to continue.

'Our ship had been wrecked. What little food we were able to save was gone. We were in desperate need of water. My sister Mary was ill. Mr Anderson took us in and, although his own supplies were limited, provided for us. If he had not done so, myself and others,' she looked directly at Jimmy, and waved her hand to include James Manning, 'would not be alive today.' Sir Richard Spencer nodded and she took this as permission to continue.

'Three weeks we had been there, on Middle Island, when I went to live with Mr Anderson.' A murmur rose in the hushed courtroom, but Dorothy pressed on defiantly. She found herself speaking with more eloquence and passion than she had ever done before in her life.

'And the money, Miss Newell, did you see the defendant counting it?'

'Mr Anderson was never short of money, Your Honour. He did not need to steal James Manning's forty-six pounds.'

'Forty-six pounds and fifteen shillings,' James Manning interjected, his face red and furious, his composure gone.

'Order!' called Captain Cheyne. 'Silence in the court!' Manning sat down heavily.

'And what of the second defendant, Isaac Winterbourne? Did you ever see him with the money allegedly stolen from Mr James Manning?'

Dorothy hesitated. Her thoughts had been focused on defending Anderson, not just to the court, but to her family and the whole town. She had almost forgotten the Englishman. She looked at him now. His head was lowered as if he wished to avoid her eyes. Then she spoke clearly and directly to Sir Richard Spencer.

'I never saw him with it, no. But it would not surprise me to learn that he has had a hand in this whole affair.'

At this point, the room erupted in chaos. The outraged Winterbourne began to shout at Dorothy. Manning called for both Anderson and Winterbourne to be hanged, drawn and quartered. Jimmy was spluttering, turning from one to the other, not knowing what to do next.

When order was finally restored, Sir Richard Spencer decreed that there was not enough evidence to convict either of the men. Although he had encouraged Manning to bring the charges against Anderson and Winterbourne, Sir Richard Spencer was also conscious of his obligation to conduct a fair trial. Without conclusive evidence one way or the other, the case must be dismissed. There was no doubt in the magistrate's mind that this was what the law required.

James Manning vehemently declared it to be a miscarriage of justice and departed soon afterwards to continue his much-interrupted journey to the Swan River Colony. Anderson was free to go.

45

'I MUST SET THINGS RIGHT AT HOME,' DOROTHY SAID TO ANDERSON as they held each other tightly in the cave that had become their meeting place.

'How long?' he asked.

'Perhaps a month,' Dorothy said. 'But promise you will come back for me.'

'Always,' he said.

The whaleboat was loaded. The crew, having heard the news of Anderson's release, had suddenly materialised to reclaim their positions. Winterbourne, in the bulky coat Dorothy had seen on him in court, shifted impatiently on his thwart. Gimble stood barefoot in the shallows, his hand on the rocking gunwale, ready to push the Beetle out into deep water, while the others sat waiting for Anderson to take up the steering oar.

'You be real set on stayin', then?'

'Please, you know I can't leave today. Not with my mother ill and my baby brother still coughing his heart up. Netty is clearly not able to manage the house and the children on her own.' Anderson studied Dorothy's anguished face, the deep furrows between her eyes. 'Will you come back?' she pleaded.

He reached out and took her hand. Although weathered and roughened with work, Dorothy's skin looked incredibly white against Anderson's liver-hued palm. He closed his fingers gently over hers and leaned towards her ear. His scarred cheek brushed her hair.

'You know I will,' he said. She smiled then. The tight lines of her face softened and her cheeks flushed with colour.

'Soon?' She stretched up on her toes and kissed him.

Her thoughts flew to Middle Island. She remembered the day they arrived, more dead than alive, in the *Mountaineer*'s whaleboat and her first sight of the proud, impervious black figure standing above the beach, the undisputed ruler of all he surveyed.

Since her return to Albany, Dorothy had been reminded of how much she enjoyed the company of women like herself. Fun-loving young women, including her sisters, Netty and the fast-maturing Caroline. And she could see that there was now a sense of optimism, of hope for future prosperity in the town which, when she left it, had been a loose collection of starving settlers. But she could not see Anderson as part of that town.

He was the acknowledged ruler of Middle Island, where he guarded his solitude and his freedom with equal ferocity. A man at home on the sea, not a farmer, a shopkeeper, a builder. While there was a part of her that longed to share that freedom and the wild beauty of his kingdom, to take comfort from his strength and give succour to his children, Dorothy knew that she could not abandon her own struggling family. Not yet.

Now, in the clear light of day with the men looking on, she would not allow herself to cry. She steeled her back, raised her chin and watched him sail away.

46

IN THE ROUGH-HEWN COTTAGE OVERLOOKING THE HARBOUR AT King George Sound, Patrick Taylor scanned the pages of notes that he had made. 'A terrible business, Mr Gimble – terrible.' There was a pause while the JP repaired his quill and produced a clean sheet of paper. When he was ready to resume the task they had begun several hours before, he looked sternly across his table at Nimble Gimble who sat opposite, head bowed. 'But, if I have heard you correctly, a murder has been committed. And while I fully understand your reluctance to speak of it, especially since these men are still at large and you are known to them, we can not turn a blind eye to this sort of thing. It is important to all of us – to the future of our town – that criminals be brought to justice. So, I beg you to continue. From the day of your departure, two years ago, from King George Sound, if you please, Mr Gimble.'

'I never trusted Isaac Winterbourne. Not from the first time I set eyes on him to the last.' The ageing sailor twisted his woollen cap fiercely in his hands as he spoke. 'Oh, he was clever with the words right enough. And he knew that Anderson needed someone to watch his back, after Bathurst went home to America. But I reckon he always planned to kill him, from that day on. Anderson was smart, though.'

Gimble went on to explain that, with Dorothy and William Church always around the hut and the clearing, and no firearms allowed on the island, except Anderson's own, Winterbourne would have had to do the deed in the whaleboat, in front of Anderson's crew. He would be badly outnumbered, for there was not a man among them who would risk crossing Anderson on the high seas. So Winterbourne began to whisper little doubts in the ears of the more recent arrivals – Mead, Hill and the like. Then he stole James Manning's money and tried to make it look as though Anderson had done it. And he spread the story that Anderson had a stash of loot he hadn't told anyone else about. Money that should have been divided evenly but had all gone in to Anderson's own sea chest. That didn't wash with most of the men. Anderson was a hard man. But he looked after his own. Besides, there was only one boat. Anderson was an excellent sailor, but no one believed he was up to taking a four-man Beetle out to sea, making a raid on a fully crewed ship and getting back to Middle Island before anyone else had noticed. Clearly, Winterbourne had mutiny on his mind. And he could be very persuasive.

When Anderson had taken Dorothy Newell as his mistress, there had been some grumbling among the men. But no one could match Black Jack's quick thinking, his skill as a seaman or his strength and cunning in a fight. His crewmen knew that they owed their survival and prosperity to him. Women were secondary. They were patient men. They wouldn't have survived more than a few days on Middle Island if they had not been, and their wealth made them attractive in any port. They could find their own women.

Gimble went on to tell of the riotous celebrations, the drinking, gambling and whoring that continued well into the night on that last visit to King George Sound. Anderson, while not exactly sober, had been unusually quiet, going off on his own for hours, returning after midnight. They all guessed where he had gone and would not deny him his pleasures. But when Dorothy decided to stay on with her family in Albany, there was a sense of relief among the men. They thought that, back on Middle Island, things would soon return to the way they used to be.

On the voyage back, there was a lot of banter and light-heartedness – except from Anderson, who stood at his oar, scowling at the horizon and saying not one word.

When they finally beached the boat in Goose Island Bay, Biddi, Nurla and Johnno were there to greet them. The new supplies were rolled in their barrels from the beach to the hut. The flour was broken into and fresh damper made.

As soon as Johnno had sighted the approaching whale-boat, Biddi had added more meat to the tammar stew. A warm, hearty smell had already filled the hut by the time the men landed.

At the end of the meal, the new barrel of rum was broached.

Tired from the journey, and a little drunk, Gimble spread his bedroll early. He had chosen the furthest corner of the veranda, to be away from the noise and the risk of being stumbled over when the men went outside to relieve themselves, and had quickly fallen into a deep sleep.

47

A SINGLE SHOT RANG OUT.

Jolted awake in the darkness under the veranda, Gimble thought at first that he had dreamed it. Then a long keening cry, like that of an animal in deep distress, issued from inside the hut. He leapt up and made for the door.

The kitchen was in chaos. Stools were overturned, mugs strewn on the floor. The curtain had been torn down from the doorway so that Gimble looked straight into Anderson's private room.

A second shot cut off the scream and felled Biddi. Her body spreadeagled across Anderson's chest. Their blood pooled together on the hard dirt floor.

Mead and Hill were crouching on either side of Anderson, pinning his arms as he lay in his bed of sealskins. Their faces registered deep shock. They seemed frozen, unable to move. A hole had been blown in Anderson's head. Blood, cerebral fluid and bits of bone speckled the arms and chests of his two crewmen.

Isaac Winterbourne was also in the room. He was bending over Anderson's sea chest, pulling it towards him, hammering at the lock with the butt of a still-smoking pistol. When the screws finally gave way he flung open the lid, throwing papers and a battered copy of the Bible out onto the floor.

'It's not here!' Winterbourne screeched. Straightening up, he braced the pistol and waved it at Mead and Hill. They continued to stare dumbly, unable even to lift their hands in surrender. 'The black bastard's buried it!' Swinging the pistol wildly, Winterbourne charged out into the night.

Mead and Hill covered Anderson's mutilated head with the torn curtain and fled the room. Running into the clearing, stopping, turning this way and that, they finally ran off, in different directions, into the bush.

Gimble gathered up Nurla and Johnno, who were huddled in a corner of the kitchen, clinging to each other and wailing their grief. As Gimble steered them towards the beach, they heard Winterbourne cursing and digging outside the hut at the back of the chimney.

They had reached the whaleboat and were about to launch it when Mead and Hill came up behind them. Gimble wanted to leap at their throats, to scream at them for being so cowardly, so stupid. But the need to escape from Winterbourne was more pressing and two extra able-bodied men in the whaleboat would improve their chances.

They set off in darkness under a heavy, cloud-filled sky. With their backs turned to the strip of pale sand, the blackness of earth and heavens merged seamlessly to form one enormous void into which they propelled their small boat.

They rowed in silence, dealing with their own thoughts and fears, until they reached the open sea beyond Goose Island.

'Where we headin'?' Mead asked.

'Away from here,' was all that Gimble could say. Standing in Anderson's place at the steering oar, his world suddenly shattered, he leaned over and vomited into the sea.

The moon appeared between scudding clouds, lighting the dark humps of rocks and islands as they passed, but Gimble knew every inch of the archipelago and didn't need its light. In the long days and nights that followed, Mead and Hill told how Winterbourne had secretly bought the pistol in Albany. With Anderson preoccupied by his concern for Dorothy, it had not been difficult for the Englishman to smuggle both weapon and shot aboard the Beetle, bandaged to his body and hidden under his large coat. When Anderson had asked about the extra padding, Winterbourne had said he had been in a fight at the pub and one of his ribs was broken.

With no provisions on board the whaleboat and the weather deteriorating rapidly, the mismatched party was eventually forced to land on Bald Island, about a day's sailing from King George Sound. They collected rainwater and killed seals for food while waiting for calmer conditions.

Another party of sealers, also seeking shelter, joined them. When they learned of Anderson's demise, they made it clear that they thought he had it coming. As far as they were concerned, natural justice had taken its course and the coast would now be clear for them to make even greater profits from selling their own catch.

Mead and Hill, who were keen for their part in Anderson's murder to be kept quiet, quickly agreed with this and convinced the other sealers to let them join their crew. Johnno, still speechless from the shock and unable to deal with Gimble's palpable grief, went with them.

Thoroughly disillusioned by the behaviour of men, Gimble stayed on Bald Island with Nurla. Their recovery was slow, but they comforted each other. They found a source of permanent water and lived very much as they had done on Middle Island. When Nurla became pregnant she recruited several other Aboriginal women from the mainland, training them in the art of herding seals, curing skins and boiling down the seal blubber for oil. Their small community grew and thrived. They took from the environment only what they needed for their survival. Gimble never worked with men again.

48

DOROTHY KNEW THAT THE FICKLE WEATHER AND THE PIRATE'S hand-to-mouth existence would make it impossible to predict when Anderson would return to Albany. But she knew he would come.

She watched for him every day as she walked along the cliff above the beach in the evening after the meal was over and the family in bed. As winter approached, she fretted over the chores. Darkness fell earlier and she became frustrated when Charles or William dawdled over their supper and refused to settle instantly into the bed they still shared.

'You miss him, don't you?' Netty said as she and Dorothy worked together, spreading the clean wet clothes to dry in the wind.

'More than I thought possible,' Dorothy told her. 'Much more.'

'Mary said he was horrid.'

'What would she know?' Dorothy snapped. 'She lay about in her bed all the time!'

Netty shrugged. 'Jimmy thinks . . .'

'The whole town knows what Jimmy thinks! Jimmy *chose*

to go ashore with Manning. Anderson gave him every chance to stay!'

'Are you in love with him?' Netty asked.

Dorothy fell silent. At that moment she would have given anything to be back on Middle Island, walking the beaches, lifting her skirt to jump from rock to rock across the point, climbing up and up through the scrub until she stood on Flinders Peak, looking out over the sea, free from the expectations of family and society, able to roam when and where she chose and come back to a good meal, warm shelter and Anderson. But she knew it was useless trying to say any of this to Netty. Their worlds had become so different.

A year passed. William was no longer a baby. Although he was still painfully thin, his cough had improved and he ran about with Charles, laughing and getting up to mischief. Netty and Caroline both found employment as servants to Sir Richard Spencer. The town of Albany had grown almost beyond recognition. Several new stores had opened and the trading post had doubled in size. Still Anderson didn't come.

Dorothy haunted the harbour. Her eyes and ears were always open, desperate for any news of him. There were rumours, of course. One said that Anderson had drowned when he fell into the sea, weighed down by his money belt full of gold. But Dorothy didn't believe it for a minute. Anderson was a strong swimmer. He had survived many mishaps at sea because of it.

It was also said that an Aboriginal woman had thrown herself overboard and drowned with him. Dorothy was even more convinced that this was untrue. Biddi and Nurla were aquatic creatures, swimming with the seals as if they were of the same family.

These stories were easily dismissed. But there were also whispers of foul play, guarded murmurs of something so vicious that even the rough-living sealers were not prepared to talk about it, especially to a woman. While these rumours niggled at Dorothy, she steadfastly refused to believe them. She pictured Anderson as she had last seen him, standing tall, solid as a statue, in full command of his boat and crew. As she walked, the silver gulls wheeled above her head. She sent her thoughts winging to him, willing him to come back.

Another year went by. In her darkest moments, Dorothy began to wonder if Anderson had forgotten all about her. Had she been mistaken in her belief that he felt for her as she did for him? Having returned to his old life of fighting and drinking with the men, had he found it more to his liking? Perhaps she should have made her feelings for him clearer. At other times, when she was being honest with herself, she would admit that she had not really known how strong her own feelings were, until he sailed away.

She tried to lose herself in the daily tasks. There was still the house to run. Her father was so often absent and, unlike William, her mother's health had not improved. In fact, she seemed to be fading away before their eyes, becoming more and more isolated and withdrawn.

Physically, Jimmy had made a good recovery. But, though Dorothy often longed to share memories of Middle Island with him, he seemed vague. Sometimes, she wondered if he even recognised her, if he had blocked out all memory of that time. Among the rest of the family there was nothing but sympathy for Jimmy and his ordeal. Dorothy, too, was enormously relieved that he was alive. But she still found it difficult to forgive him for siding with Manning in court.

Then, on a blazing hot day in March 1837, she saw a familiar figure on the beach. Her heart leapt in her chest as she picked up her skirts and ran to him.

49

AS DOROTHY RACED TOWARDS THE SHUFFLING FIGURE, SHE BEGAN to doubt that it was the man she had first thought it to be. The wild mop of curly hair was more grey than red now. His movements were heavy and he lacked the agility of the irrepressible Irishman she had known. But when she stood before him, the eyes that he lifted to hers were unmistakably those of Nimble Gimble.

'It *is* you!' Dorothy barely resisted the impulse to throw her arms around the ageing seaman. Quickly scanning the beach and jetty, she asked, 'Where is Anderson?'

Gimble looked blankly at her, disconcerted and confused.

'I'm Dorothy! You must remember me. Surely I have not changed so much.' She found herself laughing, reaching for the man's arm, but stopped short of taking hold of it. There was a haunted, fearful look about him. What had happened to the jolly pirate she had known? The one who feared nothing and invariably found humour in every situation?

'Gimble?' At the sound of his name the man stood straighter, his face relaxing almost into a smile. 'Where is Anderson?' Dorothy asked again.

Gimble looked steadily into her eyes for a long moment. 'He has the freedom of the sea, as he always had.'

'Is he well? Does he miss me? Will he come and see me?' The questions tumbled over each other, helter skelter, before Dorothy could stop them. 'Oh please, Gimble, tell him to come.'

'As you know, Miss, he comes and goes as he chooses. But he is never far away.'

'Is he not with you?' Dorothy asked, becoming a little confused herself.

'He is always with me,' Gimble said, his voice cracking, breaking. 'Bald Island is home to us now. Me and Nurla. She teaches other women to herd the seals. They work as my crew. I have no more faith in men.' Suddenly, he turned his back on Dorothy and hurried away. She resisted the urge to go after him, sensing that he had said all he could – for the moment.

'Gimble is here,' she thought, nervous excitement fluttering in her stomach. 'Anderson will come.' She would not let the tiny feeling that perhaps all was not well spoil her elation. Almost skipping back to the cottage, her heart lighter than it had been in a long time, Dorothy prepared for Anderson's visit. She washed her face, brushed her hair, straightened her worn gown as best she could. The tattered clothes she wore on Middle Island had been abandoned long ago, but even now her clothes were mended and made over, sometimes two or three times. As she tugged at her petticoats, she thought of the precious notes that William Church had handed to her before he left the Sound for Van Diemen's Land to join his uncle, just one week after Anderson's trial.

'I must trust my life and my few possessions to the sea once more,' he had told her. 'These are the copies I made on Middle Island. May I leave them with you for safekeeping?'

Dorothy had gone to the wharf to see him off, wishing him well and promising to keep his papers safe.

She had not opened them. Somehow she did not want them exposed to the prying eyes of people who had not experienced the life she knew. They might misunderstand the events that Church had recorded in such detail. She thought that, one day, she would find someone to teach her. Then she would read them for herself. Meanwhile she kept them hidden, still rolled in the oiled cloth he had made from her petticoats.

When Anderson came, she would ask him if he had heard any news of William Church.

Around midnight, the wind turned to the east. It blew in through the many cracks in the walls, ruffling the hessian that hung in the doorway and making the coals glow in the fire-place of the cottage above the harbour.

Dorothy stirred in her chair by the fire. Leaning forward, she shifted a log from the side to the middle of the grate. The fire danced with new energy and threw its warm shadows on her face and hair. Pulling her shawl more closely around her, she huddled into her high-backed chair, for she felt a sudden breeze.

As she sits, dreaming, her thoughts swirling and settling, a man comes up from the sea. He strides purposefully, his giant frame held erect, head high, chin thrust forward. When he enters the house he sees that she is sleeping and breathes a long, deep sigh. The curtains move in the breeze.

He goes around the cottage, checking the windows, the doors, the hatch where the wood is passed in from outside.

When he is satisfied that all is secure he returns to the sea. But he will come back. Always.

Epilogue

AFTER ANDERSON'S DEATH, ISAAC WINTERBOURNE SEEMED TO DIS-
appear. He certainly had all the necessities of life at his disposal
and may have continued to live in hiding, among the islands of
the Archipelago, for many years.

The Newell family remained in Albany. Hannah Newell
died 'from drinking spirits' in 1839.

Dorothy Newell (born Dorothea, to James and Hannah
Newell in 1814) lived a long and varied life and died in 1886.
She was 'married' three times. She is recorded in January
1837 as Dorothier (sic) Anderson, mariner's wife, then in the
1850s as Dorothea 'Dolly' Cooper, wife of James Cooper,
although no official record of either of these marriages has
been located. After 1855 there is no further mention of James
Cooper, but in 1875, Dorothy's marriage to George Pettit,
farmer of Albany, was officially recorded. Then the picture
again becomes blurred. Although George Pettit died in 1892,
some six years *after* his wife, Dolly Pettit is described as 'an
old maid' who took in boarders and also ran a bakehouse and
confectionery store. She is referred to in the diary of Kate
Keyser, another Albany resident at the time, as: 'a woman of

property and yet it is said she died of neglect and starvation. Poor old thing, she had no children to care for her.'

Sightings of the ghost of Dolly Pettit, and the man who comes up from the sea to keep her safe, have been consistently reported over the years. Dolly Pettit's house became Kooka's Restaurant for a time, and is now preserved as part of the Stirling Terrace Heritage Precinct in Albany. Those who presently have their offices in the building report hearing heavy footsteps ascending the stairs to the landing on the first floor where Dolly's ghost warms herself in front of a (now disused) fireplace.

Sheets of paperbark, carefully rolled in oilcloth, were reportedly found among Dolly Pettit's possessions after her death on 22 January 1886. These sheets apparently contained William Church's notes. Even then the ink had faded, but once the powdery sheets were unrolled and exposed to the air they deteriorated very quickly and have since been lost.

William Church himself boarded a ship bound for Van Diemen's Land in October 1835.

James Manning set off for the Swan River Colony, but there is no official record of him being there in the 1830s.

Nothing more is known about John Bathurst or Reuben Anderson.

Author's Note

I BASED THIS FICTIONAL ACCOUNT ON KNOWN FACTS, BUT AT TIMES the evidence was sketchy at best, and occasionally I altered details to suit the story I wanted to tell.

The man known in Australia as Black Jack Anderson almost certainly used more than one name during his eventful life. Those who were evading the law, and there were plenty of them in the remote frontier colonies, often changed their names to conceal their identity. There is some evidence to suggest that Black Jack Anderson, who signed his name 'John William Anderson' at his trial in 1835, also used the name 'John Williams'.

Efforts to trace him in America have so far led nowhere. The births and deaths of African-Americans in the early nineteenth century were often not recorded. I believe that the Free Man of Colour, Reuben Anderson, on whose details I have based my account of Anderson's early life, was Black Jack Anderson's father, but so far it has been impossible to verify this.

Settlement in Western Australia at the time of Black Jack Anderson was in its infancy. Only a small percentage of the population could read and write, so recordkeeping was a rather haphazard business. The spelling of people's names varied, even in official documents, and there are often conflicting reports of major incidents. Where I have found this to be the case, I have used the account that is most closely supported by other written material, or most logical and credible, given what we do know about the lives of seafaring men in those times.

But the Declarations of James Manning and James Newell, as dictated to Sir Richard Spencer in August 1835 and the Declaration of Robert Gimble to Patrick Taylor on 29 May 1837, have survived. As has the letter sent by Sir Richard Spencer to the Colonial Secretary containing details of the trial of Anderson and Winterbourne, and the record of Dorothy Newell's statement in court during the trial. These documents are in the records of the Albany Courthouse and the Colonial Secretary.

I also drew on information from articles published in the *Perth Gazette* in 1835 and 1842, other Western Australian newspapers and magazines between 1959 and 1992, the published research of Graeme Henderson (marine archaeologist with the West Australian Maritime Museum for many years) and the reference list in Sarah Hay's novel *Skins*, which opened up new avenues for my own research.

There are several references to George Merredith and Mai in books about the early days of settlement on Kangaroo Island. (See reference list.)

The quote from William Church's notes in Chapter 24 came from the 5 January 1933 *Western Mail*.

The first of many articles about Black Jack Anderson was written by W.N. Clarke and appeared in the *Perth Gazette* on 8 October 1842. There is also a reference to the *Perth Gazette*, 3 October 1835, but copies of the weekly publication from 15 August to 17 October are missing from the Battye Library collection. The article *Black Anderson: a story of the South Coast* by 'Polygon' (Albany Library) may have come from there.

Stories about Black Jack Anderson and the events on Middle Island during the 1820s and '30s have been passed on for generations by word of mouth and in written form. Some of these stories I found in the archives of the Esperance Museum and the Historical Societies of both Esperance and Albany.

In order to experience the settings described, I travelled extensively, spending time on Middle Island, in Esperance and around King George Sound. In all of these locations people were extremely helpful and eager to tell their own stories of the notorious Black Jack Anderson. I thank them sincerely for being so generous with their time and have endeavoured to mention them all in the Acknowledgements.

Acknowledgements

MY THANKS TO DON MACKENZIE, WHO RELATED TO ME THE STORIES of 'Black' Anderson that he heard from his father and grandfather, to Tristan Mackenzie, who introduced me to Don, and to the other members of the Mackenzie family who took me to Middle Island and shared many stories and historical details of the area with me.

Also to Dorothy André of the Esperance Bay Historical Society (Inc.), who carries an amazing reference system in her head and generously guided me through the archives of the Esperance Museum.

Jenni Carter, Sue North and the team at the Battye Library, where the whole treasure trove of information about Black Jack Anderson first opened up for me, facilitated my extensive research, and Corioli Souter and staff at the Fremantle Maritime Museum provided copies of the most recent reports of their archaeological work on Middle Island.

In Albany, Barbara Templeman, Malcolm Tuill and Julia Mitchell of the Albany Library were enormously helpful. Iain and Jo Macinnes gave me access to Heritage Council documents and retold the ghost stories associated with Kooka's

Restaurant. Sergeant John McBeath showed me around Dolly Pettit's house and shared his recent experiences of the ghostly inhabitants of the building. He and Dave Murphy were also very helpful in locating details of the way trials were carried out in the early days of settlement in Western Australia.

I am indebted to Lisa Riley, Jane Godwin and Laura Harris at Penguin Books for their encouragement. But my greatest debt of gratitude is to Catherine McCredie, whose meticulous attention to every detail has rescued me time and again. Lesley Reece, Mailee Clarke, Kylie Power, Jenni Doust and the staff of the Fremantle Children's Literature Centre I thank for their continued support.

To Peter Forrestal, what can I say? As always, he has been endlessly supportive and provided wisdom, encouragement and a carefully selected supply of red wine. Thanks.

References

Articles

Esperance Express 8 December 1992 p. 2 b. 16822298

Esperance Traveller Autumn 1987 p. 22 and Autumn 1990 p. 43,
    919.417 ESP

Perth Gazette 8 October 1842 (article by W.N.Clarke)

Weekend Mail 13 June 1959 p. 6 b. 175240 39

The West Australian 20 July 1974 p. 21 b. 1674696X

Books

Bolster, W. Jeffrey, *Black Jacks: African American Seamen in the Age
    of Sail*, Harvard University Press, Cambridge, Mass., 1997

Chase, Owen, *The Wreck of the Whaleship Essex*, Review, London,
    2000 (diary of Owen Chase first published New York, 1821)

Cumpston, J.S., *Kangaroo Island: 1800 – 1836*, Roebuck Society
    Publication, Canberra, 1970

Ericson, Rica, *Dictionary of Western Australians Vol. 1 Free Settlers*

Hay, Sarah, *Skins*, Allen & Unwin, Sydney, 2002

Knowles, Lee, *Serocco Days*, Fremantle Arts Centre Press, Perth,
    1993

Melville, Herman, *Moby Dick*, first published as *The Whale*, London,
    1851

O'Murray, Keith, *First There Came Ships*, self-published, 2004

Pease, Z.W., *The Catalpa Expedition*, Hesperian, Berkeley, CA, 2002

Preston, Diana and Michael, *A Pirate of Exquisite Mind: the life of William Dampier,* Corgi (Transworld), London, 2005

Rees, Sian, *The Ship Thieves,* Hodder Australia, Sydney, 2005

Rintoul, John, *Esperance: Yesterday and Today,* Esperance Shire Council, Esperance, 1986

Serventy, Vincent, *Crusoe Boys,* Fremantle Arts Centre Press, Perth, 1995

Shueard, Hallett, *Nemesis: Murder on the Southern Seas,* Peacock Publications, Adelaide, 2004

Strathem, Pamela, *Dictionary of Western Australians Volume 1, Early Settlers, 1829–1850,* Nedlands, University of Western Australia Press, Perth, 1979

Declarations

Of James Manning and James Newell made to Sir Richard Spencer on 9 and 19 August 1835, Albany Courthouse Records 1834–1841

Of Robert Gimble to Patrick Taylor, JP on 29 March 1837, Albany Courthouse Records 1834–1841

Deposition of Dorothea Newell at the trial of John William Anderson, Albany Courthouse Records 1834–1841

Documents

Diary of Captain Alexander Cheyne 1833–1855, Battye Library, Perth

Journal of Major Lockyer 1826/7, Battye Library, Perth

'Mackie, William Henry (1799–1860)', *Australian Dictionary of Biography* – Online Edition, for information about how the law was administered in the colony in 1835

'Register of Heritage Places: Interim Entry', Heritage Council of Western Australia, for the history of Dolly Pettit's house

rant/rave/review/win

between
the lines

betweenthelines.com.au